STEAM TRACTION ENGINES, WAGONS AND ROLLERS IN COLOUR

by
BRIAN JOHNSON

LONDON
BLANDFORD PRESS

First published 1971
© 1971 Blandford Press Ltd
167 High Holborn
London WC1V 6PH

ISBN 07137 0547 7

Filmset by Keyspools Ltd, Golborne, Lancs.
Printed and bound in Great Britain by
C Tinling & Co. Ltd, London and Prescot

CONTENTS

For the steam engine owners of Britain,
whose efforts have ensured the survival
of so many fine engines.

INTRODUCTION

Every year close on a million people visit a steam traction engine rally in Britain sometime during the summer months. These iron monsters, once cursed by all but a few as dirty, slow, noisy and inefficient machines for carrying the nation's produce or doing a whole host of useful tasks, have now in their retirement attained popularity with young and old alike as holiday entertainment. It is strange indeed that a machine which spent all its working life fighting official and popular prejudice against it should, in the end, have such an enthusiastic following.

Through this book I hope to show in a non-technical manner the history of the traction engine, its various uses and designs and at the same time possibly capture the spirit of the unexplainable 'bug' which makes one an enthusiast of these machines and want to preserve them. Questions to engine drivers usually ask what the various parts of the engine do and how it all works, so I will attempt to answer some of these points with the aid of the colour plates which illustrate the many different types of engine built and their manufacturer's characteristic designs.

May I wish all readers many happy days at steam engine rallies in the future amidst the clouds of steam, the aroma of hot oil and the glitter of polished brasswork with all those special, distinctively traction engine sounds to delight the ear. If your visit is the more enjoyable for having read this short account my task will be complete.

Worthing,   Brian Johnson
1971

PART 1   THE TRACTION ENGINE
How the Traction Engine Works

The steam engine has been in common use for over a century and a half but, as any traction engine owner will tell you, one of the most frequently asked questions about an engine is how does it work, closely followed by the wits who enquire if the water is to put the fire out or whether the fire is to keep the driver warm. That the basic workings of an engine have remained a mystery to most people for so long is most surprising as railway engines, which work on a very similar principle, were an everyday sight until just a few years ago.

Everyone will have noticed how boiling water gives off steam which if trapped will try to force its way out of its container – the bouncing kettle lid is a good example. In simple terms a traction engine works by harnessing this steam power and controlling the escape of the steam in a manner which makes it do useful mechanical work. Reference to the engine parts diagram (see page 24) will make the explanation easier to follow.

The main part of most traction engines is the boiler which consists of three sections; at the rear end is the firebox which will be seen just forward of the rear axle on most designs; the centre section is the boiler barrel which is fastened to the front plate of the firebox; and the smokebox which is the final segment of the boiler barrel supports the chimney. This design of boiler is known as the locomotive type and is the most commonly used design in traction engines.

The firebox is made of steel plate riveted together and forms a box shape with the bottom end open where the firebars or grate is fitted on which the fire rests. The firebox is surrounded on all except the bottom side by a water jacket which connects through with the boiler barrel section so water may move freely from one to the other. The boiler barrel has inside it a large number of tubes the open ends of which protrude into the firebox at one end and into the smokebox at the other so the hot gases from the burning coal may pass from the fire to the smokebox and away up the chimney. All the tubes are surrounded by water and a level is maintained in the boiler so that all the tubes and the firebox are totally submerged at all times. A plate known as the front tube plate is fitted between the smokebox and the boiler barrel section so no water can escape into the smokebox section. Heat from the fire is transferred through the firebox sides and from the surface of the tubes to the water thus heating it eventually to a temperature at which steam is produced. The tubes, with their large heating surface, soon raise the water temperature and as more and more steam is produced the pressure within the boiler rises so that when most engines reach their working pressure there is a pressure of around 150 to 200 pounds per sq. inch available in the boiler. Most engines will move slowly on as little as fifty pounds pressure of steam but how the steam actually moves the engine is another mystery to many people.

There are only two ways the steam can get out of the boiler (unless a disaster occurs!), one being through the safety valves fitted on top of the cylinder block, which will allow the steam to escape to the atmosphere should too much be produced in the boiler and the pressure rise above that at which the engine was designed to work. Without this valve it is quite possible the boiler would explode if the pressure rose too high. The other way out for the steam is through the regulator valve situated within the cylinder block which regulates the amount of steam released very carefully to the working parts of the engine. From the regulator the steam passes to the valve chest where valves worked by the linkages from the main crankshaft of the engine direct the steam at the required moment into the cylinder. If, for instance, the piston in the cylinder is at a point near the end of the cylinder, steam will be admitted on the side of the piston nearest to that end and its pressure will push the piston back down the cylinder. As the piston moves the first inlet valve will close and as soon as the piston reaches the far end of the cylinder, the valve gear will open another inlet valve at that end on the other side of the piston, thus supplying steam to push the piston back up the cylinder again. As this second stroke starts, an exhaust valve will be opened near to the first inlet valve so that as the piston travels back along the cylinder it pushes the old, used steam (which is now at quite a low pressure) out of the engine's chimney. All this mechanism is hidden inside the cylinder block and cannot be seen, but it is this action repeated rapidly which makes the piston go back and forth. The cylinder block is a very complicated casting and it is essential to the economic running of the engine that it is treated with care and the valves regularly oiled and adjusted.

The back and forth motion of the piston and its rod is transmitted to the crankshaft by means of the connecting rod and at this point the horizontal motion is converted into the rotational motion of the crankshaft. Special packings are fitted at the point where the piston rod enters the cylinder so that there is no leakage of pressure at this point. It is often a sign of a badly maintained engine if steam leaks through at this joint as any loss of pressure means a less efficient use of the steam. On one end of the crankshaft is fitted the large flywheel, the motion of which keeps the engine turning over smoothly despite the alternating pushes on the piston and the obvious 'dead' spots at the end of each stroke when the piston reverses its direction of travel in the cylinder. Without the flywheel the engine would stall at the end of each stroke and when, by chance, the engine comes to rest at this point it is known as stopping on 'top dead centre' and a restart can only be made if the flywheel is pushed around part of a turn. Also linked to the crankshaft is the linkage driving the valve gear, which on most traction engines is of the Stephenson link motion type.

The valve gear is fairly complicated and not only supplies steam at the right moment to the cylinder but is also used to determine the direction of rotation of the crankshaft. The rotation of the crankshaft determines the direction in which the engine will move, so this is a traction engine's reversing gear and is controlled by the reversing lever which may be seen on the diagram. The gear is worked by two eccentrics on the crankshaft (an eccentric being a kind of crank which converts a circular motion into a back and forth action). From these eccentrics two rods run to either end of a curved link; the upper link is the forward gear and the lower is the reverse gear. The reversing lever is connected to the curved link so that if the lever is moved forward the link drops down and the top eccentric rod will, as the engine is run, work the valve-operating rod. This will have the effect of making the engine run in a forward direction. Should the lever be pulled right back the other eccentric rod would be in line and reverse working selected; if the lever is left in a half-way position neither rod has any effect and this is the engine's neutral position. Putting the reversing lever to either extreme opens the valves on the engine fully, therefore admitting maximum steam to the cylinder which may be useful when starting but would be wasteful for normal running. In normal use a position about half-way between neutral and full is used. The valve gear and reversing lever control must not be confused with the gears which are carried on the other end of the crankshaft to the flywheel. The gears have no control over the direction of working as this is controlled by the direction in which the crankshaft rotates, which, as we have seen above, is determined by the manner in which the steam is supplied to the piston in the cylinder. A steam engine will work equally well in either direction. If this description is not clear ask a driver at a rally to show you how it works on his engine where all the various parts may be shown and demonstrated. The drive to the rear wheels on a traction engine is taken from the crankshaft through gears to the rear axle. The gears are large cogs fitted on the crankshaft and the second transmission shaft, and are forced into place by levers. Most engines have two speeds, with road engines usually being fitted with three, but in most cases, including steam wagons, gear changes can only be made at rest. On a level road any engine will start with ease in top gear with the lower ratios used for off-the-road work or climbing steep gradients with a heavy load. It must be remembered that the top speed of an engine is only in the region of six to ten miles an hour so all the ratios are very low compared to a modern car or lorry gearing. A differential or compensating gear action is usually incorporated in the transmission so that, when cornering, the outer wheel can move faster in relation to inner one and thus prevent skidding with its resulting loss of traction. The gear is often hidden behind covers to prevent mud and dust from getting on the cog wheels behind the nearside rear wheel and as the action is complex it is best viewed on an engine. The rear wheels are not actually secured to the axle but are free to rotate on it until the drive pins are inserted to lock the wheel to the axle. These pins may be seen on most engines in a bulge-like extension to the rear wheel hub. The pin passes through a flange secured to the axle to connect the drive and is removable so that the engine may be used for winching purposes. On the rear axle of many engines there is carried a drum containing a length of steel cable which may be paid out through the fairleads mounted on the tender to any item to be hauled up to the engine or, in times of trouble, actually to help haul the engine out with the cable secured to a fixed object nearby. With a driving pin removed differential action will prevent the other wheel moving, so one is left with a powerful winch mounted on the strongest part of the engine and controllable with the ordinary speed regulator.

Traction engines are basically very simple machines and most are built to the general specification noted above. There are naturally variations of design and many interesting experimental machines some of which are noted later in this book. The art of driving an engine is something which is only acquired after many years' practice and by someone with a thorough knowledge of the workings of the machine. Taking a big engine along the road in today's traffic conditions is not a job for the first-time-out amateur even though the practised driver makes it look so easy.

Driving a Traction Engine

Driving a traction engine well and economically is a job requiring some skill and a good knowledge of the actual engine as no two are exactly the same in their handling characteristics. A good deal of time has to be spent actually preparing the engine for the road before each trip and one can soon appreciate the benefits for the commercial user of the instant-starting motor lorry.

The first job in preparing an engine for the road, after unsheeting it, is to check that the boiler is filled to the correct level and that all the boiler fittings are in working order. Next the soot and dust that has collected in the smokebox and tubes must be swept out to give a clear passage for the smoke and any clinker in the firebox grate taken out together with the ash from the ashpan. Now a fire can be lit in the firebox starting with a few wood chips and small pieces of coal and gradually, as the fire gets a hold, adding the large lumps of fuel. With the fire going well and starting to heat the water in the boiler the opportunity can be taken to oil up all the motion work, fill the lubricators and grease caps on the engine and generally clean up the paintwork and brass work – a task that is seldom complete before ample steam is available to move the engine.

Before moving the engine it is good practice to let some steam into the cylinder to warm these parts as the cold metal will certainly cause condensation in the cylinder and this can be damaging. The regulator can be opened just slightly, after checks have been made to ensure the engine is out of gear, and the motion slowly turned over with the cylinder drain cocks open to release any water. This will also help to work grease and oil into all the bearings and give the driver an opportunity to check that all is well in the motion work. Several more checks must be made before the engine is taken on the road, such as the level of water in the tender and belly tanks, that the injector and water feed to the boiler is working properly and that there is sufficient coal on board.

Starting an engine is very simple. First the gear is selected and engaged by means of the levers on the driver's stand and locked in place with pins through the lever. The reversing lever is then pushed fully forward or backward depending on the direction of travel required. the hand brake released and the regulator pushed gently open to admit steam to the cylinder and take up the inevitable slack in the transmission gears as the engine starts to turn over. A further slight opening of the throttle will set the engine in motion and away you go with only the steering to worry about.

Traction engines have no brakes in the normal sense of the word on a road vehicle, although many do have a hand brake which operates on the inside rim of a rear wheel as a parking brake. At slow speeds just closing the regulator will be enough to bring the engine to rest if there is no slope to the ground, but on the road where the engine moves easily the best method is to ease the reversing lever back from its working position and close the regulator when the pumping action in the cylinder will slow the engine. In an emergency the most powerful brake is engaged by pulling the reversing lever back past its mid position and, in effect, putting the engine into reverse. This will stop the engine very quickly but also puts a great strain on the working parts and gear teeth and so is not to be recommended.

The far greater skill in taking an engine on the road comes in getting the best performance out of the engine without wasting fuel. Constant checks must be made on the fire and water level in the boiler so that sufficient steam is available at all times but none is wasted through the safety valves. In undulating country this can be quite a problem when one is constantly alternating between going uphill and then downhill. Water needs to be picked up at intervals from streams, ponds or from a hose and the wise driver will take on water at every opportunity to avoid running low.

At the end of a run the boiler pressure is allowed to drop and the fire die so that just sufficient steam is left to get the engine into its parking place. The fire can then be riddled through and the boiler water level topped up by the injector to use up the remaining steam and ensure the boiler is full for the next journey.

Many engines are two- or even three-speed machines. The gears are changed by means of the levers by the driver's stand and can only be changed whilst at rest. When changing, the engine is stopped, the hand brake or chock applied to prevent any movement, the gears changed and locking pins replaced, the brakes released and the engine moved on again. There is a danger of the engine running away out of control if this procedure is not followed as the gears form part of the main engine braking system.

The Types of Engines Built

All traction engines and steam wagons other than portable engines are designed to haul or carry goods; but even in the earliest years of their development distinctive designs can be seen and it is possible to classify groups of engines as built for specific tasks. These basic groups are listed in this chapter with a description of their main characteristics and the uses to which they were put in their working life, although it must be remembered that some engines were built as dual-purpose machines, or were rebuilt during their lives, and so can be allocated to more than one group.

The colour plates that follow have also been assembled in the same groups for easy reference and comparisons can be made between various manufacturers' efforts at producing an engine for a similar purpose.

The Portable Engine

Portable engines were the forerunners of traction engines as we know them today but, unlike their more mobile relatives which have passed from the everyday scene, the portable engine is still used in some parts of Britain. They date in their earliest form from the first quarter of the nineteenth century, developing as mobile, lighter forms of the permanent mill and mine engines then in general use. The design of the portables soon took the form in which we know them today (as shown by plates 1 to 5), with an unbroken run of production from around 1840 to very recently – indeed it is possible that a few for export are still being made.

Portables are, as the name suggests, engines which can be moved from one place of work to another as required, unlike the permanently mounted stationary steam engines which used to power many factories in the days before electricity was commonplace. The engine has no means of propelling itself along but needs some form of motive power to haul it from job to job, the task falling to large cart-horses in days gone by or tractors in more recent years. Their tasks were often connected with agriculture, with the driving of sawmills or threshing machines the most frequent work as, with both tasks of seasonal nature, the use of an engine which could be taken away in the quiet periods made economic common sense.

The engines are very simple in design as will be seen from the colour plates. The main part is a locomotive-type boiler mounted on wheels at either end with the smokebox end axle arranged on a turntable to give some steerage to the machine. Unlike most self-propelled engines the cylinder block is invariably mounted over the firebox end of the boiler with the crankshaft near to the chimney and supported on plates riveted to the boiler barrel. Virtually all portables are single-cylinder engines which, when running, gently rock the whole machine back and forth in a most restful motion. The arrangement of the engine in this layout has a great advantage with a machine designed to transmit its power via belts from its flywheels whenever it is working, as the driver has to stand by the engine controls grouped round the firebox end and is thus kept well away from the dangerous moving parts at the chimney end. He can also keep a very good lookout on the job in hand whilst he is tending the engine lest an emergency arises.

Chimneys on portables are normally very long in order to lift the smoke and any sparks well clear of the work and create a good draft to the fire. A cowl on top, incorporating a spark arrester, is also a very necessary attachment. When travelling, the chimney may be lowered by means of a hinge at its base to rest parallel with the boiler in a cradle fitted above the cylinder block – plate 4 shows this position as well as many of the controls on the engine.

The portables were built in a great size range from tiny 2-h.p. engines which could be pulled about by hand to mighty giants for export which could stand more than fifteen feet high to the top of the cylinder block. Special small engines called 'Centre engines' were also built for the showman to drive his roundabout and several of these may be seen working in these machines at old-time fairs and rallies. Coal was the most common fuel in this country but again export conditions dictated fireboxes of various sizes to cope with the burning of low-quality fuels such as straw, peat or wood with some of these entering use in this country as well. Water supply was also a problem, as no additional tank was fitted to the engines and, being static, a supply had to be bought to the working site. Most portables have a crankshaft-driven feed pump on the side of the boiler which can suck up water from a tank alongside the engine; but the water has to be brought to the tank and this was often the luckless task of the newest recruit to the team working the engine.

It is a great shame that the portable, from which most traction engines have grown, has until recently been almost forgotten in the

17

B

preservation field; but there are signs that its importance is becoming recognised in the increasing frequency of its appearances on the rally fields. There is no doubt that its use started an agricultural revolution which was later given greater impetus by the advent of the self-moving engines.

General-Purpose and Agricultural Traction Engines

Although the term 'traction engine' is used generally today to describe all types of steam-driven heavy road vehicles its early use was to describe the most common form of road steam engine, namely that used for general short-distance haulage and agricultural work. Traction engines developed from the portable engines as the inventors and engine builders applied their minds to producing an engine that could both pull itself along and haul a load. The experiments of the first half of the nineteenth century are detailed a little later on in the history of engines.

The 'traditional' English traction engine developed in the eighteen-sixties and remained basically unchanged through all its years of production until the last were built in the nineteen-thirties. The engine diagram gives a good idea of the basic features. The vehicle consists of a locomotive-type boiler, inherited from the portable engine but built to a much stronger design to survive the greater road shocks and stresses set up by the engine being self-moving. The axles are mounted at each end of the boiler with the steering axle mounted below the smokebox and free to turn about its centre point to give steerage controlled by chains fastened to each end. This unit is known as the forecarriage. The steering chains are taken back to a roller mounted on the forward side of the firebox, so arranged that when it rotates the chain is paid off one end and pulled in at the other in response to turning of the steering wheel. The arrangement may be seen in plate 13. The rear axle is mounted just to the rear of the firebox in guideways formed in rearward extensions of the firebox side plates. In many engines the axle is free to move slightly vertically and sprung by means of heavy leaf springs to absorb some road shocks, although this provision is not often found on early engines or ones not used frequently on the road. Mounted to the rear of the boiler unit is the tender unit consisting of the coal bunker with a water tank in its base. The space between the bunker and the firebox provides room for the driver's stand and is floored with boards. The drawbar used to anchor any trailers to the engine is fitted to the rear of the tender with, on many designs, additional strengthening bars brought round either side to the axle in order to take the pulling strain off the lightly constructed tender unit.

The single-cylinder arrangement was the most popular for agricultural traction engines; these being work horses often used by men whose mechanical knowledge was limited, its robust construction and limited number of moving parts was an advantage. However as knowledge improved and economic considerations became increasingly important the compound arrangement with its more economical use of steam and greater power began to make its mark. A notable variation was the Burrell single-crank compound which gave, in effect, the best of both worlds and was very popular as a contractor's engine. How the engine actually works was dealt with earlier. The massive motion work of the engines and ample-sized bearings ensured a long life under the worst of conditions – one has to remember that in the working days of these machines oils were by no means as good as today, whilst dust and mud were everyday road hazards.

The flywheel, normally of the spoked variety and to a design as good as a trademark for each manufacturer, had a wide rim to carry the driving belt used when the engine was in stationary use, doing such work as driving a threshing machine (see plate 45 for an example). The massive wheel was essential also to keep the engine, especially the single-cylinder type, running smoothly despite the lumpiness of the slow-revving steam engine (which may be felt when one stands next to one just ticking over). In fact the rocking motion will gradually cause the engine to sink in the ground if the surface is at all soft, and a wise driver will make sure a board is placed under the wheels before working for a long period on one spot. When working on the belt a smaller belt is connected from the crankshaft to the governors which automatically control the amount of steam entering the cylinder, thus ensuring an even speed.

The transmission on a traction engine is also very simple and very robust, some early machines only having a single speed. The gears are arranged on the crankshaft and second shaft, the selection being by means of levers worked from the driver's stand. To change gear it is necessary to stop, remove the safety pegs from the levers, change gear, replace the pegs and then move off again. As a traction engine works equally well forward or backward the gearing is the same in either direction. Most engines have two gears, with some featuring three in the transmission to the rear wheels; this has been noted in the chapter on how the engine works, and so will not be repeated here.

Most traction engines were also fitted with the rear axle winch for pulling work and guide rollers will be seen on the tenders. Few agricultural engines were fitted with canopies when new, though engines used on the road for most of their life did have some crew protection often in the form of a half-canopy. Water supply to the engine was also a problem, since refilling the tender tank was necessary every six to eight miles. For this purpose a water lifter was fitted which used boiler steam to create a suction in a hose connected to the tank, the other end of which was dipped into a handy river, pond or, illegally, horsetrough. The suction hose will be noted on many of the pictures of the engines. Getting the water from the tank to the boiler was another problem, usually solved by means of an injector; this acted by using boiler steam to create a suction on the supply pipe from the tender to the boiler. This forced the water into the boiler against the pressure already there, through a non-return valve. Some engines were fitted with force-feed pumps driven from the crankshaft.

The traction engine changed little in basic design over the years and this is possibly a cause for its eventual falling from favour as an economic machine compared to the internal combustion engines of tractors and lorries. Few engines survived still working into the nineteen-fifties, large numbers being scrapped during the Second World War.

Ploughing Engines

Ploughing engines are traction engines specially adapted for use in operating cable ploughing equipment and the term does not include the special engines, light tractors and general-purpose engines built and used from time to time for direct ploughing, or hauling the plough behind the engine.

There was a great deal of interest in the early days of steam power in applying it to ploughing and cultivating the land and it is possible the dedication of the early inventors to this aim led eventually to the general acceptance of road steam engines. Very early systems of cable plough used stationary or portable engines to haul the ploughs across the fields by means of ropes and pulleys but it was not until

John Fowler applied his thoughts to the problem that ploughing by steam, as it was later extensively practised, came into being. His first set of ploughing engines and tackle was patented in 1856 and by 1861 his own firm was building the engines to meet the big demand. A design soon evolved which, apart from improvements to detail, was not to change until the last of these magnificent engines was built in the early nineteen-thirties.

The earlier engines were all single-cylinder machines such as the example in plate 46, but later compound working was introduced, plate 48 showing a typical example. Other manufacturers produced ploughing engines but in nowhere near as great a number as Fowlers, and so few non-Fowler engines survive today.

The basic design was similar to the general-purpose engine but, on average, very much larger. The most obvious addition is the massive rope drum suspended beneath the boiler barrel between the firebox and front axle which carries a steel-wire rope neatly coiled on the drum by means of an ingenious self-coiling device invented by Fowler in 1863. The drum is driven by bevel gears on the near side of the crankshaft just by the flywheel engaging on a similar gear mounted at the top of a vertical shaft, the other end of which drives the rope drum around. Mid-way on this shaft is a dog clutch to permit the drive to be disengaged as required and this is operated by means of a lever from the driver's platform. As these engines weigh in the region of twenty tons and had of necessity to work on soft ground, they are fitted with very wide wheels to spread the load.

The engines normally operated in pairs, one each side of the field to be cultivated, and so one engine is fitted to pay its cable out on the left-hand side and the other on the right. This allows the engines to face the direction of the work along the field. The implement is attached to each cable end and is worked by each engine's alternately pulling it across the field whilst its partner allows its cable to run out freely. This method was used extensively for deep ploughing, cultivating, mole draining and ground clearing and is still used today for lake dredging, with a dredge bucket on the cable, as no better machine for the job has yet been found. The ploughing engines were used mainly by contractors who travelled from farm to farm on an annual circuit, the practice lasting up until the Second World War when the more powerful I.C.E. tractors finally ousted the engines on sheer economic grounds. A good number of sets still exist and every year are demonstrated at shows, attracting considerable interest.

Road Locomotives

The expression 'road locomotive' has disappeared from everyday use although it is still used as a legal definition, appearing in many Acts and Regulations affecting the use of vehicles on our roads. In the context of steam vehicles it is used to describe the larger road-haulage traction engines which are basically traction engines specially fitted to carry out relatively long and fast journeys, hauling big loads on hard road surfaces. This type of use for steam engines was always one of the dreams of the early supporters of the road engines who envisaged fast, heavy transport without the cumbersome and expensive track or lack of choice in routes of the railways.

The road locomotive developed in the very earliest days of traction engines, although the actual machines were of diverse and strange designs until the basic traction engine style was generally accepted. The main changes and additions for road use were incorporated to make the engine both more versatile and more acceptable on the highway, where it was a target for criticism from all quarters. Plates 53 to 63 show examples of road locomotives and the following features may be used to identify them from the general-purpose types. The engine is generally larger, with six-foot-diameter rear wheels commonplace. The motion work is hidden from view behind the motion covers or side covers which, it was claimed, prevented horses being frightened by the moving parts and passers-by from being splashed with oil! A substantial canopy was often fitted, but this was by no means universal. Engines are usually of the compound arrangement to give a good reserve of power as well as economy on the long journeys undertaken. Not visible in the colour pictures but a distinguishing feature is the provision of three-speed gearing in the transmission and springing on both axles to absorb road shocks. Extra water was carried in the belly tanks fitted on either side of the boiler barrel to give extra range between water stops – an important consideration if fast journey times were to be made – as well as reducing the chance of the engine running dry.

The road locomotive was much used to take loads from rail heads to the place where they were required or even, if the load size demanded, taking awkward objects the length of the country. Loads of 60 tons or more were not unusual, and so it was not until the mid-twenties that the first motor lorries which could compete with the steamers came into use. Special loads were almost always handled by steam with firms such as Pickfords using engines up until the late nineteen-forties, when economic considerations, the crews' working conditions and the availability of heavy, motorised haulage units finally spelt the end. The lighter road locomotives used by firms such as furniture removers lost ground to the motor lorry in the 'thirties and this has resulted in very few of these smaller engines surviving to the present day.

Showmans Road Locomotives

This specialised form of road locomotive was an adaptation of the heavy haulage engine to a particular task. If one removes the extra decoration, the twisted brass columns supporting the huge overall canopy and the dynamo in front of the chimney of a showmans engine one is left with an ordinary road locomotive, and so it is not surprising to learn that many showmans engines were once used for far less spectacular work. Examples of these engines are shown on plate 64 to 77 in the colour section.

Towards the end of the last century some showmen were starting to travel much larger fairground riding machines and the forerunner of the present cinema, which was then known as the bioscope show. As the machines grew larger and less easily transported by horses or by railway it was natural that the showman would turn to the road locomotive to haul his equipment from place to place as this was the way to move anything heavy at the time. It has never been usual for anyone in the entertainment business not to show off to attract his customers, and so the decoration of the engines to make them attractive on the road soon followed with the whole process leading to the magnificent machines produced after 1910. The first noted use of an engine was in 1859 when a circus owner hired one of Bray's traction engines to haul his circus into Folkestone, but general usage did not start until about twenty-five years later. The first engines were very simple with little decoration and small dynamos fitted on as an after-thought as the possibilities of electric lighting were experimented with. Some engines were built as mobile centres to steam-driven roundabouts but these were never common and the design soon became the accepted layout of the dynamo driven by a belt from the flywheel set in front of the chimney and an overall canopy to protect the engine. Governors were fitted, as on the threshing engines, to keep the steady speed which was most important

DIAGRAM OF A GENERAL-PURPOSE TRACTION ENGINE

R. Johnson, Jr. 1920.

Reference to the Numbered Parts

1 Smokebox door locking handles
2 Perch bracket
3 Oil lamp bracket
4 Steering chains
5 Steering gear worm wheel
6 Mudhole or washout hole
7 Damper
8 Ashpan
9 Boiler fire tubes
10 Boiler lagging
11 Lagging securing bands
12 Front wheel buffer
13 Front axle stay
14 Removable driving pin
15 Winch rope drum
16 Compensating gear mud shield
17 Step
18 Winching rope guides
19 Drawbar
20 Tender water tank
21 Coal space
22 Injector operating handle
23 Handbrake operating wheel
24 Reversing lever

25 Steering wheel
26 Flywheel brake-operating wheel
27 Regulator lever
28 Gear change levers position
   (Not visible from this side)
29 Boiler feed force pump
30 Flywheel
31 Connecting rod
32 Valve gear eccentric rods
33 Curved link of Stephenson valve gear
34 Boiler feed clackbox
35 Flywheel brake block
36 Crosshead; running in guides
37 Piston rod and valve rods (adjacent)
38 Lubricator
39 Whistle
40 Safety valves
41 Governor
42 Governor belt drive
43 Piston (valve gear omitted)
44 Cylinder front cover plate
45 Exhaust pipe
46 Front tube plate
47 Water level (diagrammatic)

to ensure a steady current supply from the dynamo. Decorations were at first only painted designs but the use of polished metal became more and more common and the styles more elaborate as showmen vied with each other to have the best-looking engine to accompany their machines. Naturally the attractions became more elaborate as well, so that the engines became correspondingly larger with truly enormous dynamos being fitted by the First World War period (see plate 65 for an example). After the war even bigger machines called for more power and this was catered for by adding an extra dynamo behind the chimney and in front of the cylinder block, driven by a belt off the main dynamo. These engines are popularly referred to as 'scenic showmans engines' as one of their uses was in powering the huge scenic railway rides then travelled by many showmen. Several engines were also fitted with cranes to lift the heavy parts of these machines by special fittings on the tender, examples of which may be seen in plates 67 and 74. The winching rope carried on the nearside rear wheel hub was used to work the crane.

The big showmans engines had a hard life during the annual travelling season; 100-mile journeys with three loaded trailers in a day were not uncommon, to be followed by many hours of work erecting and powering the rides. The last engines of this type to be built as such were constructed in 1934 (plates 71 and 77) with the last actually in use on the fairground (shown in plate 73) retiring as late as 1959.

A good number of showmans engines have survived to the present day even though some saw the last of their working days cut down to ordinary haulage engines as they were replaced by motor vehicles. Today the engines with a genuine showground history are much sought after by enthusiasts but it is regrettable that in the rush to satisfy the demand several good examples of genuine road engine have been 'converted' to the showmans style in recent years and thus further depleted the ranks of ordinary road locomotives.

Road Rollers

Although not strictly a 'traction engine' the roller is possibly the best known of all the machines which are now collectively referred to under the general name. The roller has been an indispensable machine for improving our roads for the last century and even today when the diesel roller is almost universal the name of 'steam roller' is still popularly applied to it. This surely must be the ultimate tribute to a superseded machine!

It can be said that the road roller was not constructed in its familiar form until 1865 when Thomas Aveling (founder of the Aveling & Porter company) produced a traction engine fitted with smooth wheels especially for rolling the road surface. This was a result of his observation that the passing of the heavy self-moving engines of the day along the very poor roads produced an improved surface as a result of the passage of their wide wheels. The next year another roller worked in London, with a purpose-built model supplied to Liverpool the following year. This was of very odd appearance, with a chain drive from the crankshaft of its traction-engine boiler unit to massive wheel rolls mounted either side of the boiler. Instead of the tender a massive full-width rear roll was fitted which could be steered by means of a ship's wheel on the driver's platform and the whole engine weighed in the region of thirty tons in working order.

Progress in design was rapid and within a decade the general steam roller appearance with a large front roll and strakeless rear wheels was the accepted pattern. The basic layout followed traction engine practice, so that as time went by the improvements in one were repeated on the other, including compound cylinders and various forms of valve gear. The single-cylinder roller, however, remained a firm favourite, the last rollers built in England for home use in 1946 being of this type.

The actual pressure a roller places on each unit of area of the road it is rolling is most important. In the first years of production, rollers were built to a fairly heavy weight often in excess of fifteen tons, which was very useful for crushing in stone to form a solid base but of little use on the more sophisticated surfaces of later years. After the turn of the century more and more rollers were built to the 8- to 10-ton limit with several designs of special lightweights quite popular as well. It is to the credit of the rollers that formed the base to most of our roads that their work is still standing up to traffic which the designers of that time could not possibly have foreseen. One particular design worthy of mention is the Wallis & Stevens 'Advance' roller which appeared in 1923 and was one of the few advanced steam engine designs which took account of the changing circumstances of the industry. These light rollers were very popular and are described fully in plates 133 and 134.

Tractors and Showmans Tractors

One of the restrictions in operating the large road locomotive was the fact that it needed a crew of at least two, driver and steersman, to enable safe operation and to satisfy legal requirements. Until the Light Locomotive Act of 1903 engines of all sizes had to have this crew but from that date engines with an unladen weight of below 5 tons were permitted to have only a one man crew and travel at up to 5 m.p.h. The light engines produced were known as tractors, a term which must not be confused when talking about steam engines with the more popular everyday modern use which refers to agricultural machines.

Virtually every manufacturer produced a light tractor at some time as it proved to be a most popular and useful machine. Its main features were much the same as the larger road locomotives but scaled down to the smaller size to come within the weight limit. The showmen, in turn, used decorated tractors fitted with electric dynamos in just the same way as they used the bigger engines. Indeed, the tractor proved to be an ideal machine for local general haulage work over fairly short distances, hauling trailers with ease and able to take full advantage of its greater speed and manoeuvrability. They were even used as direct ploughing engines, either towing the implement or having it actually fixed to the engine, and timber hauling was one of the jobs they were most used for.

The light tractor was naturally one of the first methods of steam transport to be affected by improvements in the motor vehicle with the result that few new tractors were built after the mid-twenties and their use had almost died out by 1939. A good number, however, survive today as a result of the engines being easily converted to light road rollers, for which there was a demand with the increasing use of lighter road surfaces in the nineteen-thirties period, just as the tractors were becoming redundant. The number of conversions back to tractors from rollers in recent years must number several dozen, with several appearing in showmans trim as seen in the colour section on showmans tractors.

The Steam Wagon

There is little doubt that the very first steam engine built for road use, Cugnot's wagon of 1769, was a steam-driven, self-propelled wagon designed to carry a load and not a traction engine. The experiments by Gurney and others with steam coaches in the nineteenth century were also basically passenger-carrying wagons, but as fate would have it the main development of steam traction in the middle and later part of that century was to be in engines designed to haul their load and not carry it. It was not until the passing of the 1896 Locomotive Act which permitted higher speeds for many light vehicles that really serious thought was again given to vehicles which carried their load.

Steam wagons developed in two distinct ways: one, known as the overtype, used a traction engine locomotive-type boiler with the cylinders, motion etc. mounted on top of the boiler, whilst the other style, called the undertype, usually used a vertical boiler with the engine mounted under the wagon floor away from the boiler. These two classes are naturally subject to considerable variation in the design and layout of the components but at least ninety per cent of wagons produced can be placed in one or the other class. The few remaining (of which it is doubtful if more than a handful exist today) are combinations of the two ideas or of quite incredible designs built in very small numbers. R. H. Clark's *Development of the English Steam Wagon* (Goose and Son, 1963) is the most useful reference work on the subject.

After early successes for the undertypes, a typical design of which may be seen in plate 151, the overtype wagon, which could call on years of experience of traction engine building, came to the fore with the Foden company producing one of the best designs in the first decade of this century. Other manufacturers did, however, continue building undertypes and interesting but quite reliable designs such as the Yorkshire made their appearance at this time. The overtype wagons, unlike traction engines, had a chassis on which the boiler rested at its rear end. The front of the boiler supported the front axle which steered in a similar manner to a traction engine although later versions adopted Ackermann-type steering whilst the rear axle was supported on springs attached to the chassis frame. Compound working was most common with many engines incorporating a double-high regulator to assist starting when maximum power was required. Traction-engine-type gears were fitted with the final drive to the rear axle containing the differential by one or two chains which were often of great length and exposed to the road's mud and dust. A small space behind the boiler formed the driver's stand with a coal supply either at one side or under the wagon body with the spare water tank. The boiler and driver's stand often took up a good half of the length of the wagon leaving a small load space, so that operators resorted to loose-coupled trailers to carry an economic load or grossly overloaded the rear axle by fitting bodies with a long rear overhang. Both these methods were unsatisfactory as they put additional strains on the wagon and coupled with the poor crew conditions this led, in the mid-nineteen-twenties, to an increasing use of undertype wagons with their longer load space on the vehicle.

Undertype wagons had a basic disadvantage in that the engine, mounted under the chassis, was prone to get very dirty with dust and mud thrown up from the wheels. The exposed motion of the traction engine was not at all suitable for these conditions although used on several of the early undertypes with the not unexpected results of great wear and tear. Light steam-launch design was very advanced at this period with neat, fast running and small steam engines which were soon modified and applied to a new role of powering a vehicle by clever designers who produced totally enclosed engines with all the moving parts protected and working in an oil bath. These units could be mounted under the chassis with no trouble and over the years reached a very advanced stage of design. Differentials were also included in the engine unit leaving only the rear drive chains open to the air (see plate 144) whilst the ultimate in design was the use of a carden shaft drive (propellor shaft) to a conventional lorry back axle not unlike those used today. Sentinel, Garrett, Yorkshire and Foden all used this method on their final designs, one of which is shown in plate 149.

Boilers on undertypes were invariably vertical types of ingenious designs. The most popular, as used on the Sentinel wagons, had a vertical firebox surrounded by a water jacket with water-filled tubes running across the upper part of the firebox. These water-tube boilers were fired from the top and had an ashpan fitted below chassis level as will be noted in plate 145. One of the great advantages of the undertype arrangement with a vertical boiler was that this type of boiler permitted a far more compact cab than on the overtype wagons and, the engine being placed out of the way under the chassis, a good proportion of the chassis length was available for carrying a load.

Overtype wagons lasted in commercial use until the early 'fifties, having been especially popular with brewery fleets, but undertypes did not finally succumb until ten years later; a few are still in use in a Sheffield steelworks at the present time (late 1970).

Special Engines

In the long history of the traction engine it must be hardly unexpected to find some engines built or rebuilt to carry out special tasks. Possibly the most bizarre were the Aveling & Porter shunting engines which were no more than traction engines mounted on railway wheels with a chain drive off the crankshaft to turn the wheels. From an appearance point of view the most unusual must surely be the special showmans engines, built with the centre mechanism of the round-about they hauled about as part of the engine over the centre of the boiler.

Plates 153 to 158 show some unusual and special engines. Plates 153 and 154 show the Garrett 'Suffolk Punch' agricultural motor of which only eight were built. This was one of the few attempts by steam engine builders to compete with the petrol-engined tractors then coming into use on farms throughout the country. Plates 156 and 155 show two designs of crane engines which today have their direct successors in the lorry-mounted mobile cranes. Plates 157 and 158 show two variations on the design of tractors, one of which, the Mann Steam Cart, met with considerable success and the other, the Robey 'Express' tractor, has only a sole survivor today. This latter did, however, show that steam vehicles need not be slow, cumbersome machines and one wonders what the result would have been had the legislators allowed the engine designers a free hand.

PART 2 THE HISTORY OF THE TRACTION ENGINE
The Experimental Stage

The story of the traction engine has all the usual ingredients of the tale of any invention which has made an impact on a country-wide scale: the trials and tribulations of the early inventors struggling to make an idea work, the successes and spectacular failures of the first machines, and the eventual triumph when the invention becomes accepted and adopted for everyday use. Where the traction engine, or any of the steam road vehicles for that matter, differs from the usual pattern is that during its working life the usefulness of the machine was never really popularly accepted and in its early developmental stages was even legislated against by Parliament. The tale is one of brilliant invention constantly thwarted by ridiculous restrictions which makes one wonder just how different our country's transport might have been if development had been allowed to proceed unhindered.

The power of steam was known in pre-Christian times but it was not until the seventeenth century that any real progress toward a self-moving steam engine was made. In 1630 David Ramsey took out a patent for a steam-driven plough, the details of which are unfortunately lost in history so that it is not until early in the next century that anything certain is known of steam engine development. Thomas Newcomen and James Watt discovered many of the principles of steam power but with their limited facilities could not take advantage of steam at any great pressure, which is most important if any engine is to move itself. Model engines were constructed in the later years of the eighteenth century; they worked quite well although there are no records of any full-size machines having been built as a result. Our first certain record of a steam road vehicle actually being built and operated on the road and carrying a load is the steam lorry built in France in 1769 by an inventor named Cugnot which, after several trips in Paris, overturned; the luckless inventor ended up in gaol as a danger to the community! A poor reward for a pioneer.

At the beginning of the nineteenth century a great deal of interest was being shown in engines to work factories and mines as well as the very early experiments in making railways work by steam. These engines relied for their power mainly on the vacuum created by condensed steam working a piston in a cylinder by suction; they were thus very slow-running, as well as heavy, and not at all suitable for road work. However, in 1801 the Cornish inventor, Richard Trevithick, built a steam carriage, followed by another in 1802, both of which worked well, carrying up to ten people. A drawing of the vehicles appears in W. J. Hughes' *A Century of Traction Engines* but again the mechanical details are not well documented. Despite the success of these vehicles, which could travel at at least double walking speed, no promotors were forthcoming and the inventor dropped the idea in favour of his world-famous work in developing mine and railway engines. About this time the first of the true forebears of the traction engine appeared as small, wheeled trolleys carrying a small steam boiler and a light steam engine mounted alongside. These engines were designed to power machines and so carried out the same purpose as the later portable engines of which we will see more anon. The next twenty-five years saw little development of the portable or steam carriage engines, owing probably to the Napoleonic Wars and the working man's increasing resistance to the new machines in factories and on the land which, it was claimed, would eventually throw everyone out of work. Any development would have been strongly resisted even if it was possible, as contemporary records of machine wrecking and similar disturbances show.

Horse-drawn carriages and wagons were still the main means of long distance or local transport in the eighteen-twenties; but the railway was daily becoming a more practical proposition and so it is not surprising to find inventors turning their talents towards producing steam-driven carriages. Unfortunately details of these mechanical carriages are not very clear although they must have been quite efficient in operation, with several in service in parts of the country separated by long distances, such as Glasgow, Gloucestershire and London. One of the most successful pioneers was Walter Hancock who, over the period 1830 to 1836, ran a service in London with his vehicles frequently averaging twelve miles an hour and even making excursions to distant places like Brighton. These runs must have been real expeditions on the indifferent roads of the time with the surfaces little better than cart tracks. The carriages had vertical, twin-cylinder engines with a chain drive to the rear axle, the steam being produced in coke-fired boilers fitted with an artificial air supply by means of a crankshaft-driven fan. (An interesting account of these

33

C

vehicles will be found in 'Vintage Commercial' magazine dated February 1963.) Further services were started at this time in other cities as well as longer distance routes in country areas, notably around Gloucester; but a well organised opposition soon put paid to further development and probably set back the growth of road transport in Britain by more than fifty years. The coaches vanished from the scene and except for some remains held in the Glasgow Transport Museum nothing appears to have survived to show us what they were actually like except for some contemporary engravings. Opposition to the road steamers was probably led by the backers of the steam railways, who saw their more elaborate systems threatened, and the owners of the Turnpike Trusts, who controlled virtually all the main roads; their cause was further improved by a series of unfortunate accidents and boiler explosions to the carriages themselves. A good cause for complaint from the road owners was that the steam vehicles greatly increased the costs of maintenance – a complaint that was to be made about traction engines later and is still made about heavy lorries today; and this resulted in extortionate toll charges being imposed on any mechanically-propelled vehicle.

The usefulness of the portable engine was being proved by a number of firms which sprang up to produce the engines, others which had been agricultural implement manufacturers joining in to help satisfy the demand. One firm, it is recorded, produced twelve engines and then ceased production as the owner said that should satisfy the demand for many years! In 1841 Messrs Ransomes of Ipswich produced what was possibly the first self-moving agricultural engine and the next year modified it so that it carried around a small threshing machine. The engine had a vertical boiler with a small engine mounted alongside it with the threshing machine also mounted on the trolley which carried the whole machine. A chain drive from the engine turned the rear axle of the trolley with the front axle working on a turntable and fitted with shafts so that a horse could steer the unit. The idea was most ingenious but failed to find a buyer. The portable continued to develop, however, with the first one built to the design we know so well today arriving on the scene from the Clayton & Shuttleworth factory in Lincoln in 1848. Claytons were over the next years to become the largest builders of portable engines in the country with the design proving to be far superior to the older style. Ransomes continued to persevere with their self-moving engine idea and in 1849 built an engine which had a surprising number of features which were found on traction engines in later years. Much must have been gained from studying railway engine design for this engine had its two cylinders mounted under the boiler barrel at the smokebox end although the drive to the rear wheels was by gears. Traction engine features were to be found in the man stand behind the firebox, the chimney at the front on the smokebox and a geared steering from the footplate to the front wheels which must have given a more positive control than most engines ever had years later. The boiler was designed for a 45 pounds per sq. inch working pressure and the engine towed a small coal and water trailer. A remarkable machine which must have attracted much comment at the time.

It is of interest to note that about this time many of the firms whose names are now familiar on smokebox doors and nameplates today entered the steam engine building industry. Several had long traditions in agricultural work, like Burrells who started in 1770, whilst others interested in applications of steam power set up their own works to make engines and agricultural tackle. Thomas Aveling is a good example of an inventor who started what was to become one of the largest firms in the business in a small country workshop in 1850. This strong link with agriculture brought about the fact that most traction engine builders' works were situated in farming communities far from the big industrial and engineering centres where one would have expected heavy engine building works. Good examples are the Burrell works at Thetford, Norfolk; Garrett's at Leiston, Suffolk, and Tasker's at Andover, Hampshire. The railway revolution also must not be discounted as this wonder of the age discouraged anyone from investing in the chaotic road system as being a place to develop a fast, comfortable means of travel, leaving the agricultural field as the only safe place to develop the traction engine.

The Traction Engine Arrives

The decade following the Great Exhibition of 1851 was one of great interest in anything mechanical, with the traction engine proving no exception. Self-moving engines started to appear at more and more frequent intervals, the majority being conversions of portables although many ingenious experiments were made, especially in utilising steam power to till the land.

Ploughing by steam power had attracted attention for some time with little real progress until John Fowler appeared on the scene. This Wiltshire man had been connected with farming all his life and foresaw great improvements in cultivation using steam power. His first attempt was in 1856, following considerable success in designing more efficient implements in the previous few years, when he arranged a ploughing demonstration using a portable engine hauling a plough on a cable via a windlass and cables running on pulleys. The implement used was a balance plough devised by Fowler, later examples of which may be seen in the colour plates in this book showing ploughing engines (plate 50). Whilst the system worked it was not very efficient but further improvements won for Fowler, in 1858, the £500 prize offered by the Royal Agricultural Society for a mechanical system which could be proved more economical in use than horse ploughing. Two years later came the first appearance of a traction engine with the cable-hauling drum mounted below the engine boiler barrel and the first of the long and successful line of Fowler ploughing engines. Self-propelled engines for agricultural use were rapidly becoming more than just portable engines able to haul themselves from place to place, with the engine now powerful enough to haul its accompanying machinery as well. This brought about problems as the roads were just not strong enough or surfaced to a standard to bear the weight of these machines with a result that the traction engine was once again criticised. Road owners often blocked the road or prohibited access to engines whilst local authorities insisted on engines moving only after dark and then at two miles an hour maximum speed. The restrictions did not affect agricultural machines too badly but any attempt at building an engine for haulage purposes was a very great risk as far as the manufacturer was concerned, since a buyer was most unlikely. However this did not stop developments of road locomotives to designs which seem very strange today. One of the best was an engine devised by William Bray of Folkestone which he patented in 1856; it had a drive system consisting of short spikes which protruded through the rim of the large rear wheels to push it along. He claimed it eliminated slipping and gave good braking but omitted to mention the damage to the road! The engines were successful, with modified examples being tried by the military authorities and used in London to move large loads around, although these were of a more conventional design. Charles Burrell also built a road locomotive design, the first appearing in 1856 fitted with a special form of wheel invented by James Boydell. The Burrell engine had a conventional locomotive-type boiler with the driving axle running under the boiler forward of the firebox and fitted with enormous seven-foot wheels. A separate fore-carriage mounted ahead of the smokebox permitted steering, the whole being turned by means of a huge horizontal hand-wheel mounted directly above the axle. James Boydell's patent wheels were an attempt to stop some of the damage to road surfaces and consisted or ordinary traction engine wheels fitted at intervals around the running rim with plates hinged to the wheel at their centre point. These plates interlocked as the wheel went round so that the engine, in effect, laid its own road as it moved along. The idea was quite good and this design of wheel remained in use for many years on machines used over very soft ground; but as a practical proposition on a road locomotive it was a failure. Burrell's engine was not, however, and several were exported to India and South America over the following decade, the export market proving to be an excellent way in which proper haulage engines could be developed.

Down in Kent one of the most famous pioneers of traction engines, Thomas Aveling, was applying his thoughts to improving the self-propelling portable principle which was then the basis for most self-moving engines. His first experiments were conversions of other makers' engines, but in 1861 he designed and had built what must be the forerunner of the traction engine as we know it today. The engine departed from portable influence as the cylinders were set on the boiler barrel behind the chimney with the crankshaft over the firebox and a man stood to the rear of the firebox. In addition, to make the engine more efficient, the cylinder was surrounded by a steam jacket which kept it warm and prevented any condensation in the cylinder. This revolution in design was quickly followed by virtually all manufacturers, with tenders, tender-mounted water tanks etc. following within a year – although the steering was to remain for most of the following decade either by a horse in shafts leading the engine or by means of a separate fore-carriage turned by a steersman positioned in front of the smokebox. One of the first advances in steering was the tank-mounted wheel type, an example of which may be seen in plate 46, whilst conventional wheel steering appeared in the early eighteen-seventies.

Another important innovation on the part of Thomas Aveling was his production in 1865 of a road roller driven by steam. He had noted that the passing of a heavy engine over a stony road surface rolled in the stones and improved the surface from the rutted track state most roads were in at the time. His first roller was no more than a traction engine fitted with smooth wheels and towing a big roll, not unlike the cricket field rollers one sees today, but this was soon discarded as it was found to be of little benefit. The next year a huge machine of similar type but with improved steering was put to use with great success in London, and in 1867 the first machine designed as a roller was supplied to Liverpool. An excellent picture of this machine will be found in the story of his firm. *A Hundred Years of Road Rollers*, and what an extraordinary beast it was. The driving axle was mounted in front of the firebox under the barrel of its locomotive type boiler and driven by a chain off the crankshaft. Huge, smooth wheels were fitted to the driving axle whilst the steering was by the full width rear roll mounted in the normal tender position which was turned by means of a ship's wheel on the driver's stand. A more conventional design appeared in 1870 and set the pattern for road rollers which was not changed greatly until very recent times.

Thus, by 1870, the design of portables, road locomotives and rollers had all settled to the basic layouts which were to remain in use to the end of production of steam road vehicles. One dark cloud over the industry was, however, the 1865 Locomotive Act which its supporters must have hoped would drive the steam engine from the highway through its very severe restrictions over their operation. The Act laid down speed limits of 2 m.p.h. in towns or 4 m.p.h. in the country; engines had to 'consume their own smoke'; no visible fire on the engine was allowed; a man had to walk in front of the engine with a red flag to give warning of its approach and extensive powers were given to the road authorities to limit the use of engines. It was little wonder the railway system expanded rapidly whilst the road system stagnated.

The Heyday of the Traction Engine

Despite the legal restrictions on traction engines the production of new machines grew rapidly, with strong export markets helping the manufacturers to improve their designs in order to meet the rough conditions and higher-speed journeys encountered overseas. Many engines went to Eastern Europe converted for straw burning, ploughing engines went to Egypt and road steamers helped open up the more remote territories such as India. An interesting design of road locomotive, known as the Thompson engine, featured a vertical boiler and a single steering road wheel; an example on test in England was fitted with some of the first rubber tyres and attained speeds of twenty-five miles an hour, which showed it to be a most capable engine. Several of these engines were used in India to haul road trains before the arrival of the railways. Great advances were also made in agriculture with the engines enabling greater acreage to come under the plough and production increased by the use of machines to do tasks formerly done by hand or by horses.

A most important invention, again by Thomas Aveling, was patented in 1870 and was to further improve the design of engines. Trouble had always been experienced with self-moving engines' boilers as the stresses of the motion work coupled with road shocks tended over some time to produce leaks at seams. Aveling's invention was to extend the side plates of the firebox straight up to support the crankshaft and gearing, thus removing a great deal of the motion work induced strain from the firebox. This 'hornplate' type of design was universally adopted very quickly with increased boiler pressures and greater power resulting.

Engines were tried by the military authorities and adopted as most useful for heavy haulage; the rollers became common sights all over Britain, improving the roads of towns and country to standards unheard of before. Several variations in the design and layout of engines were tried but, with the Aveling style of locomotive-type boiler engine proving to be so trouble-free, very few of the variations were adopted or produced in any great number. More improvements were made in the quality of the materials used in the engines as technology improved and items such as wrought iron gave way to steel plate and the stronger metals enabled lighter units to be used. Costs were naturally important but at the same time a great pride was taken in producing an engine to the future owner's specification which, coupled with the fact that accurate machining tools were still in their infancy, meant that no two engines were exactly alike. Another technical advance was the production by Fowlers of a compound-type engine in the early eighteen-eighties which went yet further towards making engines more efficient although the extra expense and increased complexity of the motion work made many users favour the single-cylinder layout for many years to come.

Burrells came out with their compromise single crank compound type in 1889 and whilst this was not adopted by other makers in the way the compound double-crank system was, it was to prove a much used arrangement for agricultural engines. Gearing of engines improved, most being fitted with two ratios, and three speeds were not unusual on engines designed for higher speeds, which were not legally permitted in Britain.

The last decade of the nineteenth century saw engines in use all over Britain, and in her many colonies, performing every conceivable task of haulage on the roads or work on the land. The railways, it will be noted, expanded very little after this time and I would suggest this is to a certain extent the result of the spread of the more versatile traction engine which needed no expensive track and could deliver direct to the door loads of almost any size. Public opinion was also changing, the engine proving not to be as dangerous as first supposed, and the most restrictive provisions of the Locomotive Acts were either repealed or ignored in daily use. The red flag requirement went in 1876 although a man still had to precede an engine until the passing of the 1896 Locomotive Act, often referred to as the Emancipation Act as this was the legislation which first permitted the practical use of motor transport. The annual London to Brighton Veteran Car Run commemorates this Act, which permitted light vehicles to travel up to twelve miles an hour. Traction engines were still tightly controlled although relieved of some of the 'red tape' in operation but the greatest boost to steam heavy transport was the fact that steam wagons now became a practical possibility once again. Firms such as Thornycroft and Leyland came into the road vehicle business, the former having a good start as they were able to take advantage of their knowledge from building small launch engines to construct a very neat, small wagon engine supplied by steam from a vertical boiler of a type also used in boats. An early example of one of their wagons is shown in plate 151 and is typical of designs produced by many firms around the turn of the century, which were proving most useful for town delivery work. The first showmans traction engines also appeared about this time with the first examples being no more than road locomotives fitted with a dynamo to make electric current although the distinctive long canopies and decorations soon made their appearance. Several engines were built around 1895 with the centre supporting pole and driving gear of a roundabout built onto the engine and forming the centre of the machine when it was built up. This looked very odd and although the engines lasted quite a long time in service the idea was not pursued.

Few histories of Britain at this time make mention of the influence the traction engine must have had on industries and the countryside. The railway system was very extensive, with large quantities of goods being transported, but no mention is made of the local delivery work, the movement of outsize loads or the greatly increased productivity of the farms which can only be accounted for by the use of machines of the traction engine family. Often one reads in old documents of the arrival of new machines behind an 'engine' from the station; one I have seen noted the hauling of stones to build a monastery from the local station by 'a traction engine' whilst the annual visit to villages and farms of the threshing and ploughing gangs as well as the fair was one of the major events of the calendar. The coming of the lighter steam wagons revolutionised local delivery work, horses being replaced on all but the lightest work and places further afield being brought within a reasonable day's journey of the market. Jobs, such as timber hauling, previously carried out by teams of horses and dozens of men could be done by two engines and half a dozen men. Road rollers transformed the roads from the rough, rutted muddy tracks to solid, if dusty, all-weather roads the main base of which still serves us today with the addition of a superior wearing surface. This was indeed a revolution, but despite all the good work and benefits to the community generally the steam engine was still regarded as something everyone would prefer to be without and as a dirty, noisy nuisance.

For the men working with the engines and maintaining them it was a hard life. The story of the era is told graphically in two recent books, *I worked with Traction Engines* and *Apprenticeship in Steam* by a former steam driver Jack Hampshire, in which one gains an impression of long hours, poor pay and working conditions no-one would consider today. Much of the maintenance of engines was carried out in small workshops, often the former local blacksmith's works, with most of the work carried out by hand with hand tools and a great deal of personal skill. Traction engines were seldom built to take spare parts off the shelf, and so when anything went wrong or wore out it was a matter of making and fitting the new part. Fortunately engines were very strongly built with huge bearings so that replacements were not too frequent despite the crude lubrication systems and rough working conditions experienced. When a big job did arrive remarkable ingenuity was used to tackle the lifting and fitting of the heavy parts. It was not unusual to refit new boilers working with little more than a few hand tools and a block and tackle! The driver and his steersman too had a pretty hard life of it with working hours of dawn to dusk on the road plus the hour or so spent cleaning and oiling the engine and lighting the fire each day. The threshing and ploughing gangs were usually six-days-a-week workers travelling around with the engines and living in a van towed behind the engine which, whilst it was a life which appealed to a nomadic type of character, also attracted occasional rough diamonds with bad reputations. One feature of the worker travelling with his machine has survived until the present day, when many roller drivers can still be found moving around with their roller and living on the job site in a van (very frequently one of the old steam-engine-towed vans still in use) which travels with the roller.

The twenty years following 1900 were probably the best for the traction engine. Relieved of many of its restrictions it was able to perform to its best advantage with the improvements in internal-combustion-engined machines of little threat to its supremacy in coping with heavy loads. Further impetus was given by the 1903 Heavy Motor Car Act which permitted traction engines of less than five tons unladen weight to be operated by one man and travel up to five miles an hour. The small locomotives built by virtually every manufacturer to take advantage of this were called tractors (see examples in plates 79 to 90) and soon proved to be best sellers, ousting yet more horses from haulage work. A second generation of steam wagons also appeared on the market about this time known as the overtype wagon. These had traction-engine-style boilers and motion work built into a lorry chassis, the final drive to the rear axle being by chains. The most popular builder of this type of wagon was the Foden company, as the large number to survive into preservation days testifies, but they were built by many other firms as well.

Engine design naturally continued to improve but few revolutionary designs reached the drawing board, much less the customers, the standard layout adhered to being more than thirty years old. The resulting machines are magnificent examples of British craftsmanship, the standard of finish even today worthy of study as examples of elegant simplicity. The lack of development was, however, to prove a grave disadvantage in the rapidly changing world of the next twenty years.

The Demise of the Traction Engine

One of the first blows to the supremacy of the traction engine and steam wagon as the obvious choice for any heavy road haulage came in the years just prior to the First World War. Steam road locomotives had been used by the military authorities for the past fifty years in all parts of the world and had showed themselves to be quite capable under the trying conditions of Africa during the Boer War around 1900. Experiments continued throughout the first ten years of the new century including unusual machines such as the Fowler caterpillar-tracked traction engine but a real surprise came in 1911 when a subsidy scheme for buyers of motor lorries was announced. The scheme was intended to give the Army a good supply of transport at short notice and owners taking the subsidy had to guarantee they would supply their vehicle with a driver for service at forty-eight hours notice should any trouble occur. This naturally gave the motor vehicle industry a great advantage and when the War came the Army selected motor lorries as its main transport. The disadvantages of the steam wagons were obvious as they were much heavier, needed more attention, had bulky fuels as well as being difficult to get on the move at short notice. Fodens built a good number of wagons for military service during the war but the number was small in comparison with the huge number of motor vehicles built both in Britain and imported from America. Meanwhile at home steam vehicles literally kept the country going with most heavy transport being by steam and large numbers of general purpose and ploughing engines being built to help boost the transport supply and food production. Heavy road locomotives too were required both at home and abroad as there was no replacement for these engines to move the really heavy military and civilian loads.

Thus the fateful 'twenties arrived with the traction engine builders just starting to feel the fall off in orders after the furious activity of the war years and the Government depots full of good surplus motor lorries which could be picked up for a song. Even on the farms a new machine had made its appearance with numerous paraffin tractors popping and banging their uncertain ways around the fields carrying the strange names of American firms whose products were unknown in the pre-war days. The motor vehicles' success in the later years of the war was well known and now there were plenty of them for anyone who wanted one.

The effects on the traction engine building firms were soon to show as orders fell off for the small tractors, but many firms hoped their customers would support them with new orders for the larger engines and these certainly flowed in for the first year or so. A new design which had been on the market since just before the war came into its own at this juncture, the Sentinel undertype wagon proving to be a most reliable vehicle which could be guaranteed to move at least as big a load faster and more economically than a motor lorry of similar dimensions. The up-to-date, fully enclosed underfloor engine, good driver's cab and easily maintained boiler were all points in its favour, beside the fact that the available load space exceeded that of almost any other lorry on the road. Several other makers such as Garretts tried similar designs with some success whilst others such as Fodens carried on with their overtype wagons which even then looked a little old-fashioned. Roads, too, were improving at this time with better surfaces calling for road rollers of a lighter type than the heavy models then in general use. The problem was answered by the conversion of many of the light tractors made redundant by the large number of motor lorries available but Wallis & Steevens Ltd of Basingstoke produced a revolutionary new design called the Advance roller which appeared in 1923. This roller was designed specifically to deal with softer road surfaces and featured an instantaneous reverse, wide rolls, light weight and a very smooth running twin-cylinder engine. Examples of these rollers may be seen in plates 133 and 134.

Another market which received a boost at this time was the building of showmans road locomotives with fairground owners requiring bigger and bigger engines to haul around the huge fairground rides then in vogue. The engines built were really fine machines and even today the sight of one on the road is impressive and memorable.

However the industry in general was not doing well. The depression was imminent and orders were getting harder and harder to find. Several firms pulled out of the industry or carried on only doing repairs, whilst others tried new ideas or improved wagon designs to try and boost sales, usually with little effect. It was inevitable that mergers would occur, the biggest being the Agricultural & General Engineers combine led by Thomas Lake Aveling and including Burrells and Garretts. This was a most unhappy association as each firm tried to keep its identity, its products and its factories going as before with only the Aveling & Porter firm doing anything different from previous practice. Avelings did start building engines to jig designs in order to simplify the number of parts and work on replacements, as well as introducing several good new roller designs which sold well.

Burrells and Garretts finally merged, but this did not save the group which crashed in 1932. The Aveling & Porter branch alone was saved by the intervention of the Barford brothers, Ransomes, Sims & Jefferies and Ruston & Hornsby, who formed Aveling-Barford Ltd out of the ruins to survive to the present day. Many other firms also gave up about this time but it was the East Anglian communities, suddenly cut off from the major employer in the town, who suffered most with the mismanagement of the firms at this time still bitterly regretted in the area.

The gloomy picture was not improved in 1930 when the Road Traffic Act of that year laid down new restrictions on heavy vehicles, the most disastrous as far as the traction engine was concerned being the restrictions on axle weights and licensing charges based on the unladen weight of the vehicle. No measure deliberately designed to push engines off the road could have been worse than this, as most engines were heavy and had high axle loadings; so large numbers of excellent traction engines and wagons were sent to the scrapyards as unusable, with no compensation to their owners.

Many firms naturally turned to the production of motor lorries with Fodens, who had designed a magnificent undertype wagon in 1930, known as the Speed Six and capable of sixty miles an hour fully laden, and had abandoned steam in 1932. Sentinels continued to develop their wagon; a new design appeared in 1933 looking much like a motor lorry and certainly as good, as the example shown in plate 149 will show. A few traction engines continued to be built but buyers were almost non-existent, a typical example being the last Foster engine which although built in 1933 was not sold until 1937. Steam rollers continued to be in demand with Aveling Barford producing new designs after their merger, Fowlers, Marshalls and Wallis and Steevens providing a choice for the prospective buyer. Portable engines were still in demand, especially in export markets, and these continued to be produced well after the Second World War for both home and foreign use. The steam wagon died slowly during the 'thirties as the larger motor lorries became more efficient, the Sentinel being the last to go in 1939—although a new model working on a revolutionary high-pressure steam principle was tried after the war and a few export wagons were delivered around 1950 to South America.

Our tale finally draws to a close in 1948 when Aveling Barford produced the final batch of home-market steam rollers and after a period of over a hundred years of continuous production the building of road steam vehicles for home use finally finished in Britain.

The Preservation Era

Few regretted the passing of the steam road vehicles from everyday use. The motorised tractors and lorries rapidly replaced the engines, to such an extent that by the early nineteen-fifties very few remained in service anywhere in the country. They were, no doubt, far more economic, faster, cleaner and easier to work with but the loss of the 'character' of the old steamers was regretted by many drivers. For a strange reason steam engines have a fascination to many people and a character of their own which it is almost impossible to describe. You soon know what it is though, when the 'bug' bites, and then it is too late to avoid it! In the same way as railway engines have been followed for many years by enthusiasts, the traction engine had its followers who, faced with the disappearance of their interest after the Second World War, started to rescue some of the old engines from a scrapyard fate. Even then many of the older, more interesting examples had gone, but a remarkable number have survived through individual efforts. Engines around 1950 were virtually worthless with even the big showmans engines selling for a few pounds only, so that anyone who wanted one had little trouble in obtaining a good example.

In these early preservation days efforts were mainly uncoordinated, owners taking engines out for a run just for the fun of it; but after 20 August 1950, following a race between two friends on their engines to which quite a crowd had been attracted, the rallying of traction engines was really started. The winner of that race is shown in plate 31. Since those days the interest has grown rapidly, with societies forming all over the country to run rallies and allow anyone who likes seeing and talking about engines to meet occasionally. The rallies now attract in the region of a million people a year to events all over the country with the displays ranging from small gatherings at village fêtes to mammoth displays showing engines working at ploughing and threshing, sawing wood or just carting loads of goods about the field.

In recent times the actual racing of engines has died out as it did place strains on the machines which the designers never intended, as well as proving dangerous to anyone standing nearby if something went wrong. Today, displays showing the engines working at the jobs they were built for are much more popular with most visitors to the events seeing the tasks performed for the first time in their lives. Naturally, the price of engines has risen as the demand has increased and the number of engines derelict has fallen to almost nil. Restoration costs are very high, since few firms are able to carry out the skilled work required in repairing an engine, and just keeping an engine in good condition is a full job in itself. Several newcomers have found this out the hard way to the dismay of their wives and bank managers!

Unfortunately, no national collection of engines exists in one museum, and so to see the development and types of engine one has to travel around several summer rallies in all parts of the country to get anything like a complete picture. I hope this book will help anyone interested in noting the types and makes to identify them for himself. One fascinating collection does exist in the collection of engines built by Taskers of Andover which, it is hoped, will be put on public display in a purpose-built museum near Winchester as soon as sufficient funds are available. This will be a unique display, the setting up of which is worthy of every enthusiast's support.

This brief history of the traction engine is naturally only an outline of the whole story of their development. Numerous books now exist describing particular types of engine or detailing the history of a particular manufacturer to which the interested student is directed for further study.

PART 3   THE COLOUR PLATES

The colour plates which follow are arranged in groups according to the type of engine illustrated. Each group is arranged in alphabetical order of manufacturer and each manufacturer's engines (where applicable) are arranged in date order. Below each plate is given the reference number of the plate, the maker's name, the date the engine was built and the engine number. Full details of the engines illustrated follow the plates arranged under the plate reference numbers.

The engines illustrated are grouped as follows:

Particular engines may be found by looking under the manufacturer's name in the main index on page 177.

1 **Marshall** portable engine No. 534154, built 1912.

2 **Clayton & Shuttleworth**
portable engine, built 1867.

3 **Foster** portable engine
No. 201, built 1870.

4 **Brown & May** portable engine
No. 8262, built 1900.

5 **Tuxford** portable engine
No. 1131, built 1883.

6 **Allchin** traction engine No. 669, built 1890.

7 **Allchin** traction engine No. 1527, built 1911.

8   **Allchin** traction engine No. 3251, built 1925.

9   **Aveling & Porter** traction engine No. 6601, built 1906.

10   **Aveling & Porter** traction engine No. 8401, built 1914.

11   **Aveling & Porter** traction engine No. 9096, built 1920.

12 **Burrell** traction engine No. 3068, built 1908.

13 **Burrell** traction engine No. 3201, built 1910.

14 **Burrell** traction engine No. 3655, built 1915.

15 **Burrell** traction engine No. 4048, built 1926.

16 **Clayton & Shuttleworth** traction engine No. 46817, built 1914.

17 **Clayton & Shuttleworth** traction engines Nos. 36336, built 1904, and 46823, built 1914.

18 **Clayton & Shuttleworth** traction engine No. 48154, built 1917.

19 **Foden** traction engine No. 9502, built 1914.

20 **Foster** traction engine No. 3682, built 1909.

21 **Foster** traction engine No. 14625, built 1931.

22 **Foster** traction engine No. 14637, built 1936.

23 **Fowell** traction engine No. 108, built 1922.

24 **Fowler** traction engine No. 7459, built 1896.

25 **Fowler** traction engine No. 10373, built 1905.

26 **Fowler** traction engine No. 11491, built 1908.

27 **Fowler** traction engine No. 15771, built 1926.

28　**Garrett** traction engine No. 28410, built 1910.

29　**Garrett** traction engine No. 34561, built 1931

30 **Marshall** traction engine No. 15391, built 1887.

31 **Marshall** traction engine No. 37690, built 1902.

32 **Marshall** traction engine No. 52280, built 1909.

33 **Marshall** traction engine No. 84562, built 1926.

34   **McLaren** traction engine No. 547, built 1894.

35   **McLaren** traction engine No. 1160, built 1912.

36 **Ransomes, Head & Jefferies** traction engine No. 5137, built 1878.

37 **Ransomes, Head & Jefferies** traction engine No. 5137, built 1878.

38 **Ransomes, Sims & Jefferies** traction engine No. 38088, built 1927.

39 **Ransomes, Sims & Jefferies** traction engine No. 41046, built 1930.

40 **Ruston Proctor** traction engine No. 35501, built 1908.

41 **Ruston Proctor** traction engine No. 36828, built 1909.

42 **Wallis & Steevens** traction engine No. 7293, built 1913.

43 **Wallis & Steevens** traction engine No. 7248, built 1914.

44 **Wantage** traction engine, built *c.* 1914.

45 **Marshall** traction engine No. 45872, built 1906, driving a reed comber threshing machine.

46 **Fowler** ploughing engines Nos. 1368, built 1870, and 2013, built 1873.

47 **Fowler** ploughing engine No. 1368, built 1870.

48 **Fowler** ploughing engine No. 13880, built 1913.

49 **Fowler** ploughing engine No. 14213, built 1914.

50 **Fowler** ploughing engines Nos. 15210 and 15211, built 1918.

51 **Fowler** ploughing engines Nos. 15344, and 15345, built 1919.

52 **McLaren** ploughing engine No. 1552, built 1918.

53 **Aveling & Porter** convertible engine No. 5800, built 1905.

54 **Aveling & Porter** traction engine No. 5862, built 1905.

55 **Burrell** road locomotive No. 1945, built 1896.

56 **Burrell** road locomotive No. 3593, built 1914.

57 **Fowler** road locomotive No. 9381, built 1902.

58 **Fowler** road locomotive No. 9456, built 1902.

59 **Fowler** road locomotive No. 12693, built 1911.

60 **Fowler** road locomotive No. 14754, built 1917.

61 **Fowler** road locomotive No. 14754, built 1917, on the road.

62 **McLaren** road locomotive No. 1424, built 1913.

63 **McLaren** road locomotive No. 1652, built 1919.

64 **Burrell** showmans road locomotive No. 3443, built 1913.

65 **Burrell** showmans road locomotive No. 3509, built 1913.

66 **Burrell** showmans road locomotive No. 3886, built 1921.

67 **Burrell** showmans road locomotive No. 3909, built 1922.

68 **Burrell** showmans road locomotive No. 3938, built 1922.

69 **Burrell** showmans road locomotive No. 3979, built 1924.

70 **Foster** showmans road locomotive No. 14502, built 1921.

71 **Foster** showmans road locomotive No. 14632, built 1932.

72 **Fowler** showmans engine No. 11799, built 1909.

73 **Fowler** showmans road locomotive No. 14425, built 1916.

74 **Fowler** showmans road locomotive No. 15653, built 1920.

75 **Fowler** showmans road locomotive No. 15657, built 1920.

76 **Fowler** showmans road locomotive No. 20223, built 1934.

77 **Fowler** showmans road locomotive No. 20223, built 1934.

78 **Aveling & Porter** tractor No. 11480, built 1926.

79 **Aveling & Porter** tractor No. 11486, built 1926.

80 **Burrell** tractor No. 3191, built 1910.

81 **Foster** tractor No. 14514, built 1922.

82 **Fowler** tractor No. 15632, built 1920.

83 **Garrett** tractor No. 33986, built 1920.

84 **Marshall** tractor No. 73900, built 1920.

85 **McLaren** tractor No. 1837, built 1936.

86 **Ransomes, Sims & Jefferies** tractor No. 39127, built 1928.

87 **Robey** tractor No. 37657, built 1918.

88 **Ruston Proctor** tractor No. 52573, built 1918.

89 **Tasker** tractor No. 1296, built 1903.

90 **Tasker** tractor No. 1309, built 1904.

91 **Wallis & Steevens** tractor No.   ?   , built 1903.

92 **Wallis & Steevens** tractor No. 7641, built 1921.

93 **Wallis & Steevens** tractor No. 7881, built 1927.

94 **Aveling & Porter** showmans tractor No. 7612, built 1912.

95 **Aveling & Porter** showmans tractor No. 7899, built 1913.

96 **Burrell** showmans tractor No. 3894, built 1921.

97 **Foster** showmans tractor No. 13036, built 1913.

98 **Fowler** showmans tractor No. 21221, built 1937.

99 **Garrett** showmans tractor No. 31193, built 1913.

100 **Robey** showmans tractor No. 41492, built 1923.

101 **Tasker** showmans tractor No. 1822, built 1920.

102 **Armstrong-Whitworth** roller No. 10R19, built 1923.

103   **Aveling & Porter** roller No. 2941, built 1892.

104   **Aveling & Porter** roller No. 6378, built 1907.

105 **Aveling & Porter** roller No. 6893, built 1909.

106 **Aveling & Porter** roller No. 9108, built 1920.

107 **Aveling & Porter** roller No. 10594, built 1923.

108 **Aveling & Porter** roller No. 11675, built 1926.

109   **Aveling & Porter** roller No. 14070, built 1930.

110   **Aveling Barford** roller No. AC 606, built 1946.

111 **Babcock & Wilcox** roller No. 95/4009, built 1926.

112 **Burrell** roller No. 4018, built 1925.

113 **Burrell** roller No. 4070, built 1927.

114 **Clayton & Shuttleworth** roller No. 48946, built 1924.

115 **Fowler/Allen** roller No. 8111, built 1905.

116 **Fowler** roller No. 16100, built 1924.

117 **Fowler** roller No. 19032, built 1930.

118 **Fowler** roller No. 18075, built 1930.

119   **Green** roller No. 1968, built 1914.

120   **Mann** roller No. 1145, built 1915.

121   **Marshall** roller No. 68955, built 1916.

122   **Marshall** roller No. 79669, built 1925.

123 **Marshall** roller No. 81095, built 1926.

124 **Marshall** roller No. 88096, built 1937.

125 **Robey** roller No. 42216, built 1925.

126 **Robey** tandem roller No. 42520, built 1925.

127 **Robey** tri-tandem roller No. 45655, built 1930.

128 **Ruston & Hornsby** roller No. 115124, built 1923.

129 **Tasker** roller No. 1409, built 1909.

130 **Tasker** roller No. 1902, built 1923.

131 **Wallis & Steevens** roller No. 2656, built 1903.

132 **Wallis & Steevens** roller No. 7799, built 1924.

133 **Wallis & Steevens** 'Advance' roller No. 7962, built 1928.

134 **Wallis & Steevens** 'Advance' roller No. 8100, built 1934.

135 **Foden** steam wagon No. 10530, built 1921.

136 **Foden** steam bus No. 11340, built 1922.

137   **Foden** steam wagon No. 13008, built 1928.

138   **Foden** steam wagon No. 13716, built 1930.

139　**Foden** timber tractor No. 13266, built 1928.

140　**Foden** tractors Nos. 12852, built 1928; 14078, built 1932; and 13238, built 1929.

141 **Garrett** wagon No. 35465, built 1931.

142 **Robey** wagon No. 42657, built 1921.

143 **Sentinel** wagon No. 1286, built 1916.

144 **Sentinel** wagon No. 5509, built 1924.

145　**Sentinel** tractor No. 5558, built 1924.

146　**Sentinel** wagon No. 8213, built 1930.

147　**Sentinel** wagon No. 7954, built 1929.

148　**Sentinel** timber tractor No. 8777, built 1933.

149 **Sentinel** wagon No. 9075, built 1934.

150 **Tasker** wagon No. 1915, built 1924.

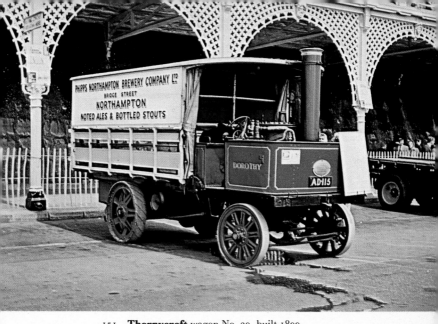

151 **Thornycroft** wagon No. 39, built 1899.

152 **Yorkshire** wagon No. 652, built 1914.

153   **Garrett** 'Suffolk Punch' tractor No. 33180, built 1918.

154   **Garrett** 'Suffolk Punch' tractor No. 33180, built 1918.

155 **Burrell** crane engine No. 3829, built 1920.

156 **Ransomes, Sims & Jefferies** crane engine No. 31066, built 1921.

157　**Robey** 'Express' tractor No. 43165, built 1927.

158　**Mann** steam cart No. 1287, built 1918.

Descriptions of the Engines Illustrated

1 Marshall 8-h.p. portable engine No. 534154, built 1912

The main features of the portable engine are seen clearly in this picture. The single-cylinder engine is mounted over the firebox and the cast, open-sided tubular crosshead guide is alongside this on the crankshaft side. The driver stands by the firebox end where the firehole door can be seen and he is holding the regulator lever. Large ball weight governors are fitted to give steady running speeds to the belts driving off the very elegant curved spoke flywheels. The tall chimney is fitted with a spark catcher whilst for transit the whole unit can be lowered by means of the hinge near its base, the top resting in the cradle fitted to the top of the cylinder block.

2 Clayton & Shuttleworth 8-h.p. portable engine built 1867. Maker's number not known

Clayton & Shuttleworth Ltd were the largest builders of portables in the mid-nineteenth century. This engine shows the main features of these very simple single-cylinder engines. It will be noted that the crankshaft and cylinder positions are reversed compared with a self-propelled traction engine. Steerage is by the axle at the chimney end and in the early days it would have been fitted with shafts for a horse to pull the engine about. The double flywheels enable the engine to drive two machines if required – this particular machine worked in a sawmill, being one of many thousands used for this task.

3 Foster 4-h.p. portable engine No. 201, built 1870, *Great Tew*

This is a typical portable of the period. Note the very large ball weight governors and the boiler feed pump worked by an eccentric on the crankshaft to lift water from the barrel alongside the engine. Also visible on the firebox front plate is the gauge glass showing the boiler water level.

4 Brown & May 5-h.p. portable engine No. 8262, built 1900

This view shows a portable ready to be moved on to its next job with the smoke-stack lowered on to its rest. The governor belt may be seen running from the crankshaft to the governors mounted on the valve side of the single-cylinder block. On the firebox front plate can be seen all the controls which are, from left to right: two water level test cocks, regulator lever, pressure gauge, whistle and water gauge with the cylinder drain cocks operating lever just above. At the base below the firehole door are the water drain cock and the ashpan damper. The maker's name appears on the decorated cylinder end plate.

5 Tuxford 1½-h.p. portable engine No. 1131, built 1883

Possibly one of the smallest portable steam engines made for commercial use, this engine shows a typical feature of early types in the use of polished wood lagging around the cylinder. The equipment on the side of the boiler is a water lifter used to keep the boiler full whilst running.

This engine is an exhibit at the Cheddar Motor Museum.

6 **Allchin traction engine No. 669, built 1890, AP 9081,** *Bess*

This is the oldest Allchin engine still in existence and is a 7-n.h.p., single-cylinder, three-shaft engine. The large diameter boiler is typical of the older engines, especially singles, which ran on lower steam pressures than the later engines. A good head of steam was available on this occasion as the safety valves are well lifted in this view of the engine about to set off on a journey. A rather plainly designed chimney is fitted whilst the good display of rally attendance plaques fitted on the tool box shows this to be a very active octogenarian! The paint style and colours are copied from those applied to the engine when it was new.

7 **Allchin traction engine No. 1527, built 1911, CF 3650,** *Felicity*

A very fine example of a 7-n.h.p. single-cylinder Allchin which has been in the same family ownership since its appearance at the Royal Show when new. The Allchin company was one of the smaller firms which did not build a very great number of engines and this one can be described as a completely 'traditional' design. The maker's name and engine number will be found on the rectangular plate on the cylinder block side.

8 **Allchin traction engine No. 3251, built 1925, NU 7483,** *Royal Chester*

Royal Chester was the last traction engine built by Allchins and is a 7-n.h.p. single-cylinder, slide-valve machine. It has been restored to the form in which it was to have been shown at the Chester Show when new although it never actually appeared there. The design is typical of later general-purpose engines.

9 **Aveling & Porter traction engine No. 6601, built 1906**

Aveling & Porter, although best known for their road rollers, built a great variety of types of engines especially in the pre-

First World War days. This is an example of the 6-n.h.p., single-cylinder, slide-valve traction engine which has a rather low-slung appearance not uncommon in engines of this make. The rampant horse is the trade mark of the manufacturer and is well to the fore on the smokebox door.

10 **Aveling & Porter traction engine No. 8401, built 1914, AF 3427**

A 6-n.h.p. double-crank compound general-purpose engine typical of many thousands used for threshing, agricultural work and haulage. Useful identification features of an Aveling engine are the maker's oval name and numberplate found on the cylinder block side. Note also the ample-sized inspection manhole on the boiler side, the spud pan on the front axle and rounded profile to the smokebox door.

11 **Aveling & Porter traction engine No. 9096, built 1920, AF 6001,** *Jubilee*

This is a 6-n.h.p., two-speed compound engine mounted on springs and fitted with rubber tyres which would make it a very versatile general purpose engine. In its working days this one was used for threshing and haulage work for which full-length canopies were often fitted to give the engine and crew some protection. This type is easily confused with the road locomotive but note that no extra belly tanks, motion cover plates, heavy flywheel or three-speed gear are fitted. Several of the bolt-on spuds are being carried on the front-axle spud pan in case of wet ground conditions necessitating their fitting to the rear wheels.

12 **Burrell traction engine No. 3068, built 1908, AH 5978,** *Victory*

Charles Burrell Ltd of Thetford built engines to a very high standard of finish and design and it is said no two were identical, as everything was built to the customer's specification. One of their finest products was the 7-n.h.p. single-cylinder engine of the type seen in this view. The most easily recognised features of this make are the chimney design and smokebox door nameplates. Two-speed gearing is visible above the rear wheel and the various operating rods of the motion can be distinguished.

13 **Burrell traction engine No. 3201, built 1910, BP 5919**

This is an example of the 7-n.h.p. single-crank compound engine which was one of Burrells' most popular designs. The distinctive cylinder block with its tall nearside fitted with two brass plates giving the maker's name and engine number contains two cylinders the front end covers of which may be seen covered with brass plates. It will be noted that unlike other compounds the cylinders are not alongside each other; the high-pressure cylinder (the smaller diameter) is set to one side and slightly above the low pressure. This arrangement permits the motion work to be simplified so that only one crank is needed on the crankshaft instead of the normal compound engine arrangement of two thus saving in original materials, work and in subsequent repairs. Most of the savings of compound working result but it is possible to stall the engine on 'dead centre'. Restoration was still in progress on the engine when this picture was taken and the boiler lagging has still to be replaced.

14 **Burrell traction engine No. 3655, built 1915, FU 822,** *English Hero*

Another variation of the Burrell general-purpose engine is shown in this 6-n.h.p. double-crank compound version. The larger cylinder block shows clearly the cylinder arrangement in contrast with the single-crank compound type shown in Plate 13. The sturdy, squat front end

and plain spoked flywheel are found on many Burrell traction engines.

15 **Burrell traction engine No. 4048, built 1926, PW 8905,** *William the II*

A 7-n.h.p. single-cylinder engine built in the next to last year of regular production by the firm. Although the two compound types had been available for many years the single still remained popular to the end. This engine has been very well restored to show condition and is seen in this view preparing to do some threshing work – the main belt is fitted, the rear wheels chocked and the governor belt lies on the top of the boiler ready to be fitted. Note also the spark arrester on the chimney without which interesting results could be obtained when threshing!

16 **Clayton & Shuttleworth traction engine No. 46817, built 1914, YA 2095**

This is a rather unusual engine, being a 'convertible' type which means that it can be used as a roller (by exchanging the wheels and front axle for roller units) or, as it is seen in this view, as a traction engine. The addition of tyres to the wheels and the full-length canopy gives it a road locomotive appearance – a true general-purpose engine! The large compound cylinder block is served by the makers unusual cross-over valve gear which is unfortunately not visible. A solid flywheel of the type often fitted to rollers has been used on this small 5-n.h.p. engine.

17 **Clayton & Shuttleworth traction engines Nos. 36336, built 1904, BP 5821,** *Peggy* **and 46823, built 1914, KE 4173,** *Dusty*

Two very fine 7-n.h.p. single-cylinder engines both showing some of the characteristic features of Clayton and Shuttleworth designs. The front axle is set well forward and includes a spud pan, the elegant chimney has a neat brass cap and two designs of the maker's nameplate are seen on the smokebox doors. The left-hand engine has an eccentric-driven boiler feed pump just above the rear wheel and has its rear wheel spuds ready on a rack. The right-hand one (46823) was used for haulage work in its working life and has a Clayton-design canopy fitted.

18 Clayton & Shuttleworth traction engine No. 48154, built 1917, NM 1161

This is a 7-n.h.p. single-cylinder engine with a long but thinner than average boiler barrel giving a low-set appearance. The usual Clayton front axle is fitted, also the dished spoke flywheel with oval section spokes of a most elegant design. This engine went new to the War Office, possibly to help with the war effort in agricultural work.

19 Foden traction engine No. 9502, built 1914, SN 1607, *Rob Roy*

Foden traction engines were never as common as their steam lorries, production ceasing at the early date of 1920. This is a 6-n.h.p. double crank compound with the distinctive appearance of all Foden engines, which were very well built if a bit more expensive than their competitors. The cylinder block is similar to those used on the famous steam wagons and carries the maker's large nameplate and engine number on its near side. A 'double high' regulator system whereby boiler pressure steam could be admitted to both cylinders is fitted giving great starting power for short periods. In this view the engine is running in reverse and the curved sliding link of the Stephenson link motion fitted can be seen in the raised position just to the left of the flywheel. Another distinguishing feature of Foden traction engines is the rear wheels, fitted with a large number of slim spokes which, it was

said, gave some springing action as the spokes flexed.

20 Foster traction engine No. 3682, built 1909, CT 3896

This is a 7-n.h.p. single-cylinder engine showing the earlier style of Foster engines. The slightly set back front axle was found on several engines built prior to 1910 and dates back to the very early days when it was thought inadvisable to use the smokebox to support the engine's weight. It also has a great advantage in creating a shorter wheelbase giving greater manoeuvrability. The driving gear is enclosed on this engine by covers to prevent excessive dust or mud getting on the gear wheels and thus causing rapid wearing of the moving parts.

21 Foster traction engine No. 14625, built 1931, VL 3465, *Barbara*

A very fine engine which could be used as a model to show the final design of the English traction engine. The engine is a 7-n.h.p. single-cylinder machine and has been finely restored to show condition after a working life in Lincolnshire.

22 Foster traction engine No. 14637, built 1936, VL 8371, *Saint*

One of the very last traction engines built in Britain. It will be noticed the design of the engine is virtually the same as engines built thirty or forty years before and it was this lack of change which helped the demise of the steam engine. The engine is a 7-n.h.p. single-cylinder machine with the characteristic flat-sided cylinder block of this make. Note the 'Tank' motif on the bottom of the smokebox door nameplate commemorating the firm's building of the first tanks in 1915.

23 Fowell traction engine No. 108, built 1922, EW 2981

The Fowell company was a small firm engaged mainly in engine repairs, but over the period 1877–1922 they built about a hundred traction engines to their own designs, some of which were most interesting and unusual. An account of the firm will be found in the N.T.E.C. 'Steaming' journal, Vol. 13, No. 1.

108 was one of the last built and is a 8-n.h.p., three-shaft, single-cylinder engine of a conventional design. The set back front axle helps give a small turning circle as well as relieving the smokebox of any strain. Two-speed gearing can be seen adjacent to the rear wheel whilst the high standard of finish is exemplified by the pleasingly shaped connecting rod visible just to the rear of the cylinder block. Only a half dozen Fowell engines now exist.

24 Fowler traction engine No. 7459, built 1896, BW 4506, *Endurance*

A 6-n.h.p. single-cylinder engine typical of the period just prior to this century from which few engines now survive. This is a typical Fowler product for general-purpose use and includes the distinctive spud pan fitted on the front axle which is also used in this case to anchor the ends of the steering chains. On the boiler barrel can be seen the painted cast iron oval design of Fowler nameplate used on their earlier engines.

25 Fowler traction engine No. 10373, built 1905, CE 7922, *Ada*

This is a 6-n.h.p., two-speed, double-crank compound engine which, in its time, was probably one of the best engines available on the market. The huge cylinder block is almost out of proportion with the rest of the engine and is the distinguishing feature of all Fowler compounds. The chimney is hinged at its base, not an unusual feature on this sort of engine, to help cleaning and storage, but is not of a Fowler pattern. Note the later design,

smaller, oval brass maker's numberplate carried on the side of the boiler barrel.

26 Fowler traction engine No. 11491, built 1908, AH 6486, *Dreadnought*

This is a very fine example of a 7-n.h.p. single-cylinder general-purpose engine, the restoration of which was completed in 1970.

The motion work can be seen very clearly with the governor, whistle, safety valves and lubricator (the black box-shaped item) mounted on top of the cylinder block. The uppermost rod seen running from the footplate to the cylinder block is the regulator control whilst below this can be seen the piston rod running to the crosshead where it meets the connecting rod (the large, rounded rod) and so back to the crankshaft. The rectangular section rods are the valve gear rods and are on the flywheel side. The crankshaft bearing brasses, which are adjustable to take up wear, are visible alongside the second shaft gears on the top of the hornplates whilst the gearing to the wheel is enclosed in the casing behind the steering shaft. The restoration of this engine shows how majestic an engine can appear without recourse to extra adornments or departing from the original specification.

27 Fowler traction engine No. 15771, built 1926, CT 8346, *George*

This is an example of the largest general-purpose engines normally used in this country and was operated on the Smiths Crisps potato-growing estates in Lincolnshire. It is fitted with extra-wide wheels to traverse soft ground. Compound cylinders are fitted to this 8-n.h.p. engine which also has the standard design of Fowler cab to give some weather protection despite it being a general-purpose engine. The chimney cap is the Fowler pattern – very plain and simple in design.

28 **Garrett traction engine No. 28410, built 1910, NO 1186, *Jolly***

An interesting comparison can be made here between the general-purpose traction engine on the right and the Garrett tractor No. 33380, built 1918, CT 4565. The traction engine is a 7-n.h.p. single-cylinder engine whilst the tractor is one of the very popular 4-n.h.p. compound engines built in large numbers by this firm. Both carry the large 'G' on the smokebox and the tractor has also the typical maker's nameplate and trade mark of a leopard. Note the very neat enclosure of the gearing and protective boards fitted alongside the firebox area on the traction engine.

29 **Garrett traction engine No. 35461, built 1931, OU 9303, *Rob Roy***

This engine has the doubtful distinction of being the last traction engine built by Garretts before the firm ceased production later in the year. It is a 6-n.h.p. single-cylinder engine of traditional appearance and finished to the usual high Garrett standards. The safety valves and governors are particularly prominent on top of the cylinder block.

30 **Marshall traction engine No. 15391, built 1887, BW 5249**

Marshalls, like Aveling & Porter, are probably best known for their rollers but they also built large numbers of traction engines of which a good number of early examples still exist. This one was exhibited when new at the Smithfield Show and has since been in the same family ownership. It is a 6 n.h.p. single-cylinder engine and in this side view the main working parts can be easily seen. Note the fully shielded driving gears behind the rear wheel and the pin in the extended part of the rear wheel hub which can be removed to disconnect the drive to the wheel. For additional support there is a bar from the front axle to the firebox front

edge helping to locate the front axle. Also visible is the towing bar which in this case is fitted to the tender rear only. The magnificent transfer on the boiler gives the maker's name and reproductions of some of the awards won by their engines at shows and trials.

31 **Marshall traction engine No. 37690, built 1902, BH 7373, *Old Timer***

Possibly the most famous traction engine of all! *Old Timer* was the winner of the first traction engine race at Appleford, Berks., in 1950 from which the present-day rallies have developed.

The engine is a 7-n.h.p. single-cylinder machine with the characteristic almost stove-pipe-style Marshall chimney and very square and solid looking cylinder block on which the rectangular maker's plate and engine number is to be found. The simple design of the smokebox door is another feature. Note also the large equipment box on the front axle and prominent lamp-mounting bracket on the smokebox side.

32 **Marshall traction engine No. 52280, built 1909, BE 7581, *Lorna***

A 7-n.h.p. compound engine fitted with a smokebox name ring advertising this fact. Note the rear wheel bolt on spuds for wet weather work hanging on the front axle ready for use and as the engine is preparing to do some belt work on a rack saw bench (just visible on the left of the picture) a large screw jack has been placed forward of the rear wheel to prevent movement. The belt to the governors can just be seen running up from the crankshaft. Note also the semi-dished design of flywheel.

33 **Marshall traction engine No. 84562, built 1926, KP 6969, *Daphne-Ann***

A 6-n.h.p., single-cylinder engine of typical later Marshall design with this view showing well the plain smokebox door, angular cylinder block and the governor set away from it to the near side. The bearing carrying the end of the crankshaft is just above the rear wheel where the golden brass colour of the adjustable parts are visible. To protect the driver from flying oil off the motion a grease guard has been fitted just to the rear of the crankshaft. This is a good example of the typical British traction engine.

34 McLaren traction engine No. 547, built 1894, BD 5448, *The Mac*

The McLaren company did not build a very large number of engines but they did build to last and their product is reckoned to be among the best. This one is believed to be their first four shaft engine built and is a 6-n.h.p., two-speed, unsprung, single-cylinder machine. McLaren engines are usually very plain with no unnecessary adornments as shown by this example finished in the maker's standard black livery.

35 McLaren traction engine No. 1160, built 1912, HO 5570, *The Favourite*

A powerful 8-n.h.p. single-cylinder traction engine with a larger than average boiler to match. This engine was an exhibit at the 1912 Brussels Exhibition where it won a gold medal before entering a working life in threshing in Wiltshire. The fitting of belly water tanks on a general-purpose engine is unusual. Note the design of the cylinder block, which is a McLaren characteristic, and also the flywheel brake fitted at its forward side.

36 and 37 Ransomes, Head & Jefferies traction engine No. 5137, built 1878

These two pictures give an indication of the amount of work required to restore an engine which has lain derelict for many years. Plate 36 shows the engine 'as found' on exhibition at the Andover rally in September 1968 and Plate 37 shows the same machine after restoration at the Beaulieu Steam Festival in May 1970.

The engine is a 7-n.h.p. single-cylinder, three-shaft machine built at a time when the design of traction engines was settling down to the now well-known general appearance after the experimental years. It is the oldest general-purpose engine still in working order and the only survivor from the days when its builder went under this name. Early features are the curved spoke flywheel, the Salter type safety valves, bolted hornplates and all exposed gearing. Originally the boiler would have been lagged with polished wood. An indication of the engine's condition when found is given by the visible holes in the smokebox. cracked chimney base and the lagging falling off – indeed a total rebuild was required down to the last bolt and rivet with a most creditable result.

38 Ransomes, Sims & Jefferies traction engine No. 38088, built 1927, DO 6883, *Enterprise*

One of only two Ransomes compound traction engines known, this is a 8-n.h.p. engine with several unusual features. The typical square chimney base of all engines of this make is fitted and the flat, except for the raised centre section, smokebox door is another identification point. The chimney top is standard but the very unusual parallel-sided chimney is a feature found only on 8-n.h.p. engines of this make. The cylinder block, unlike most compounds, does not form the steam dome the boiler steam being collected just to the rear of it and fed to it by means of a pipe. Other points of interest but not visible are the coil springing of the engine, no injector is fitted – only a feed pump and cylinder pressure release valves are fitted to prevent damage should priming occur.

39 **Ransomes, Sims & Jefferies traction engine No. 41046, built 1930, VX 7317,** *Ivanhoe*

In complete contrast to the modern electricity-grid pylon in the background is this 6-n.h.p. general-purpose engine which was one of the last built by its makers. It has several points of note such as the pipe from the cylinder block into the chimney, which is a pressure release device to prevent damage by water being compressed in the cylinder. It is released into the chimney via this pipe. The motion work and pleasantly curved flywheel are seen to advantage as is the maker's name transfer on the boiler. Note also the typical engine steering wheel with the small hand grip on the wheel edge which makes it much easier to turn the wheel rapidly, the sprung steersman's seat and the rope drum on the rear wheel with the rope guides covered by the water-lifting suction hose.

40 **Ruston Proctor traction engine No. 35501, built 1908, BE 7438,** *The Muddler*

Ruston Proctor engines are not very common, almost the majority of those surviving being portables. This is an example of their 8-n.h.p. general-purpose engine which is a single-cylinder machine of conventional appearance. It is a four-shaft engine with the crankshaft set well forward and all the gearing enclosed by dust covers. The crosshead guide is a casting bored to take the crosshead, providing a very strong guide although not so easily repairable as the more usual bar guides. The maker's badge is a simple device seen on the smokebox door.

41 **Ruston Proctor traction engine No. 36828, built 1909, KE 4991,** *Florence*

A smaller than average general-purpose engine, being of only 5-n.h.p. rating – the size can be compared with the 7-n.h.p. engine standing alongside. This is a single-cylinder machine with the maker's name and numberplate to be found on the side of the block. Strip rubber tyres have been fitted to the wheels to give a better ride on hard road surfaces.

42 **Wallis & Steevens traction engine No. 7293, built 1914, BH 6808,** *Pandora*

One of the populat 7-n.h.p. Wallis & Steevens 'Expansion' type traction engines which were produced in quite large numbers having a reputation of being economical engines in daily use. The characteristic cylinder block, front axle perch bracket and heavy general appearance are seen well in this picture. Note the boiler feed on the boiler barrel side and just forward of this a rubbing plate in case the front wheel should turn too far. These engines were usually used on agricultural work.

43 **Wallis & Steevens traction engine No. 7248, built 1914, HR 3555,** *Pedler*

An 8-n.h.p. 'Expansion' type single-cylinder traction engine which was one of a pair built for export but owing to the war never shipped abroad. It is fitted with wider than usual rear wheels to work on soft ground. This view shows well the safety valves, whistle, lubricator and governors on top of the cylinder block and boiler and also the manner in which the firebox side plates are bought up to form the hornplates carrying the crank-shaft.

44 **Wantage traction engine, built c. 1914, BW 4415. Engine number unknown**

The Wantage Engineering Company was a small firm engaged mainly in repair work; they did from time to time build an engine and two of these survive. The engines are quite conventional 7-n.h.p. single-cylinder, three-shaft, unsprung machines the design of which probably was drawn from experience of working on other engines. One interesting feature unfortunately not visible is the tender rear plate which slopes steeply away under the engine as on many very early designs. This particular engine lay in a scrapyard for over thirty years until retrieved in 1968 when it was so rusty few expected it ever to run again. Much hard work by the owner, however, saw it in steam and at its first rally in July 1970.

45 Marshall traction engine No. 45872, built 1906, driving a Marshall threshing machine

This view gives a very good impression of the working conditions many engines used by agricultural contractors would have worked in. The engine is belted up to the Marshall threshing machine placed alongside the stack of wheat to be threshed. The engine has its governor connected by a belt to the crankshaft in order to keep the machine running at a steady speed. This threshing machine is fitted with a reed-combing device so that the individual pieces of stalk are not smashed to pieces and can be collected after the threshing process for later use for thatch. In the foreground an earlier form of threshing using a flail is being demonstrated. The picture was taken at the 1970 Blandford Steam Working.

46 and 47 Fowler ploughing engines No. 1368, built 1870, AL 8468 *Margaret* and No. 2013, built 1873, AL 8463, *Noreen*

This pair of ploughing engines are the oldest active traction engines in Britain. They date from the first decade of steam ploughing under the two-engine system invented by John Fowler and are the design which set the pattern for virtually all future ploughing engines. They are single-cylinder types of 12-n.h.p. and do not, at first glance, look very different from any other ploughing engine. However small items such as the safety valves

show their age and an interesting feature seen on Plate 46 (1368) is the alternative speed gear carried off the countershaft and kept on the walkway board alongside the motion until required. A real case of cog changing! The other view shows another early feature of these engines – tank steering. The steersman can be seen on the back of the tender pulling round the horizontal steering wheel which has to be turned right to go left and *vice versa*. Also visible on the boiler barrel is the old-style Fowler nameplate.

48 Fowler ploughing engine No. 13880, built 1913, NO 371

This is an example of the AA-type Fowler ploughing engine of 18 n.h.p. Nearly all the ploughing engines now existing are of this general design or the 16-n.h.p. BB version being built in the first twenty years of this century with the greatest number dating from the First World War due to government support at this time for new tackle.

The magnificent profile of the Fowler can be judged in this view. Many enthusiasts think these engines are the most elegant of all the types built and they certainly give an aura of gentle power. A compound cylinder arrangement is fitted with polished cylinder head caps on the front of the massive block. The crankshaft and two-speed transmission are clearly visible leading to the offside rear wheel and the large cable drum is mounted under the boiler barrel being driven on the nearside of the engine adjacent to the flywheel. Nearside steering is fitted. In order to accommodate the rope drum and provide access to the ashpan side damper flaps are fitted to the firebox. Other points of note are the exhaust pipe from the cylinder block passing to the chimney atop the boiler; the hinged chimney allowing the engine in low sheds or under tree boughs and the front axle-mounted tool box containing the spuds for the rear wheels should muddy conditions prevail and require their use.

Plate 48) are the slightly smaller smoke-

49 Fowler ploughing engine No. 14213, built 1914

This is an example of the BB version of the Fowler ploughing engines. The main differences from the AA version (see Plate 48 are the slightly smaller smoke-box and single slide bars for the piston rods; the engine is rated at 16 n.h.p.

This view shows the arrangement of the cable drum driving gear adjacent to the flywheel with the large bevel gear clearly visible just below the flywheel hub. When this gear is meshed with the gear on the crankshaft it drives the vertical shaft on which there is a dog clutch to engage the drive to the drum – this clutch can be seen just below the flywheel rim with its red operating lever running up to the driver's position. The steersman's position is set well back as plough engines needed double manning anyway. The flywheel is of a distinctive dished spoked design found on all Fowler ploughing engines.

50 Fowler ploughing engines Nos. 15210 and 15211, built 1918, AD 8990 & AD 8991, Hengist and Horsa

This view shows a pair of ploughing engines preparing for a days work at the 1970 Blandford Steam Working in Dorset where steam ploughing was demonstrated. The engines are raising steam; hence the rather dark smoke from the new coal on the fire whilst the crews are oiling up the motion. The engines are BB1 types of 16 n.h.p. They went new to the War Department and later saw service with two ploughing contractors.

The plough is a Fowler six-furrow anti-balance unit. The cable from the right-hand engine can be seen passing into the centre section to fit on the axle – a similar cable would be paid out from the other engine when it is on the opposite side of the field. On the raised

section of the plough can be seen the ploughshares and a steering wheel and driver's seat. When the furthermost engine pulls on its cable the ploughshares are pulled down into the ground and the steersman riding the plough can steer the whole unit into the correct line. The other end of the plough lifts clear at the same time so that two-way ploughing can be achieved. As the plough cannot be pulled right up the edge of the field a headland is left after the engines have passed which can be finished either by turning the engines at right angles to their normal working or finishing by other ploughing means.

51 Fowler ploughing engines Nos. 15344 & 15345, built 1919, NM 429 & NM 430

A fine pair of Fowler ploughing engines. Most engines of this type were built in pairs to work the two-engine system of ploughing or cultivating and stayed together all their working lives.

This pair shows all the usual features (for notes see Plates 48 and 49) of a BB-type set. The stark chimney is a typical feature and the smokebox door nameplates are a type found on most larger Fowler engines – the actual engine numberplate is the oval brass plate on the boiler barrel and can be seen on the nearest engine just below the inspection gangway. The large steel disc hanging on one of the lamp brackets is a chimney cover for damping down the fire overnight or preventing rain falling down the chimney when the engine is out of use.

This pair of engines is still used occasionally by their owner for lake dredging purposes.

52 McLaren ploughing engine No. 1552, built 1918, BD 5504, Hero

This is one of the very few ploughing engines not built by John Fowler Ltd which are still in existence in this country. It has all the usual ploughing-engine features such as wide wheels, massive appearance and large gearing which can be clearly seen leading from the crankshaft down towards the rear wheel. It is a compound engine and has the usual McLaren design block and rather plain front end appearance. The steering is fitted on the offside. Due to the fact that the original winding drum under the boiler was missing when the engine came into preservation a Fowler one has been fitted as a replacement.

53 Aveling & Porter convertible engine No. 5800, built 1905, BP 6043

This Aveling & Porter engine is a type which can be converted to either a traction engine or a roller (see also Plate 106). The additional bracket to support the front mounting for the roller can be seen around the top of the smokebox door.

The muddy conditions at the time this view was taken have resulted in the owner fitting the extra bolt-on spuds to the rear wheels to give extra grip. These additions are illegal on the road as it is not difficult to imagine the damage they would cause to any surface. Also of interest in the background is an engine working on a belt with the governors in 'full flight' visible between the flywheel and cylinder block and keeping the engine running at a steady speed.

54 Aveling & Porter traction engine No. 5662, built 1905, KE 7490, *Emma*

A 7-n.h.p. double-crank compound engine which spent most of its early life on heavy haulage work and has been kept in preservation in its original road use form. Most of the fittings of a road engine are present other than additional belly water tanks and a very strong canopy is fitted. Note the typical Aveling nameplate, chimney and flywheel designs.

In the early days nearly all engines ran on straked wheels such as those on this engine but later rubber tyres became more popular as they helped reduce road shocks on the engine at the higher speeds then permissible. By the 'twenties most road engines had been fitted, but the general purpose engines retain the strakes to the present day.

55 Burrell road locomotive No. 1945, built 1896, CF 3355, *Sparkie*

This is a 6-n.h.p. engine and one of the oldest road engines still in existance. The conversion to showmans' style was carried out during restoration in 1958 but the basic engine is unaltered. Burrell features can be seen in the style of the smokebox nameplates, cylinder block, chimney cap and wheel design whilst closer inspection would reveal the excellent finish found on all engines of this make.

56 Burrell road locomotive No. 3593, built 1914, KE 3865, *Fidus Achates*

A 6-n.h.p. double-crank compound engine with the easily recognised Burrell design of cylinder block and nameplates. This is a typical road engine with a three-quarter-length canopy of Burrell design, solid flywheel and full-width belly tank on which can be seen the water-lifter and suction hose as well as the pocket-type filler through which the water level can be seen or a hose placed to fill the thank. These engines were very well finished and on this example the extensive paint decoration has been faithfully reproduced.

57 Fowler road locomotive No. 9381, built 1902, WR 6770, *Perdita*

One of the larger, 8-n.h.p., three-speed, compound road locomotives built by Fowlers and popular with heavy-haulage contractors all over Britain. Engines of this type worked on all heavy-haulage jobs until the early nineteen-fifties – this particular one worked up to 1963 and was one of the last engines of any type in commercial use.

It will be noted the motion covers are not fitted, and so the connecting rods etc. can be seen and a belly tank is also absent. The spud pan on the front axle was often used as a 'junk box' where all sorts of useful spares could be kept. The long canopy is of Fowlers' pattern and was fitted to all types of engine built by them.

58 Fowler road locomotive No. 9456, built 1902, KK 3634, *Jess*

This view shows the form in which many of the earlier road locomotives were used when new, without the overall canopy. The heavy, undished flywheel suggests a two-speed engine and is of Fowler pattern. This is a 6-n.h.p. compound, slide-valve engine which worked on both haulage and fairground work before being restored from a derelict state.

59 Fowler road locomotive No. 12693, built 1911, FJ 1850, *Brunel*

A Class D2 engine which is a 5-n.h.p., three-speed, compound machine and a representative of the smaller types of road engine of which very few exist today. All the usual Fowler features can be seen whilst the smokebox nameplate is of interest being a type found in the main on this maker's smaller engines.

60 Fowler road locomotive No. 14754, built 1917, NO 459, *Endeavour*

A typical Fowler road engine. The engine is a compound with the distinctive Fowler design cylinder block which enclosed the cylinders within a steam jacket to give greater efficiency. The cylinder head covers in burnished alloy and the side of the block covered with a polished brass cover are also features of this make for road engines. These are three-speed engines with the heavy, dished flywheel to accommodate the full gearing. Other points to note are the chimney cap, brass-

edged motion covers and the maker's plates.

61 Fowler road locomotive on the road

A sight rarely seen in the nineteen-seventies! Fowler road locomotive 14754 described in Plate 60 out on the road complete with the crew's living van in tow.

This engine completed the run from London to Brighton on the 1970 Historic Commercial Vehicle Club Run – a journey of over 50 miles completed in under seven hours. It is seen here pulling away after an oiling-up halt near Hand-cross.

62 McLaren road locomotive No. 1424, built 1913, BE 7518, *Captain Scott*

An 8-n.h.p., three-speed, compound engine which has seen use on both road haulage and agricultural work. This was probably the most popular size of heavy road locomotive and the size can be compared with the traction engines on either side. The spoked flywheel and small belly tanks are unusual although the former might be a replacement. An unusual feature on this engine is the use of bolted-on blocks of rubber on the rear wheels to provide some cushioning effect to the road surface as, although this method was quite common in earlier times, it is very rare today.

63 McLaren road locomotive No. 1652, built 1919, WF 1864, *Boadicea*

This is a magnificent example of the largest size of road locomotive built for normal use in this country, although bigger machines were exported. It is a 10-n.h.p. compound engine built originally for the War Office for artillery haulage, into which form it has been restored. Note the very large rear wheels, heavy solid flywheel, motion covers and belly tanks typical of the big road engines and also the opening hatch in the cab roof to give ventilation under the low canopy.

Despite the wisespread use of motor vehicles by the military at the time this engine was built, really heavy loads still required the power of steam engines.

64 Burrell showmans road locomotive No. 3443, built 1913, CO 3822, *Lord Nelson*

A fine example of the Showmans-type road locomotive. This one was built for Messrs Anderton & Rowland and worked around the West Country. The basic engine is an 8-n.h.p., double-crank compound road locomotive to which has been added the smokebox extension to carry the huge electric dynamo and the large overall canopy with its twisted brass support columns. Note also the extra decoration of the flywheel (which has a wide rim to take the dynamo drive belt), the motion covers, belly tanks and cylinder block. The large black object on top of the roof is an extension piece to the chimney fitted when standing generating to carry away the smoke up above the adjacent fair attractions. An interesting feature is the Westinghouse steam pump unit on top of the belly tank which makes use of the boiler steam to pump water up into the tanks on the engine. Originally these engines ran on straked wheels, but they were all fitted with rubbers in the 'twenties.

65 Burrell showmans road locomotive No. 3509, built 1913, G 6469, *Rajah*

This small 5-n.h.p. road locomotive was used by Bostock & Wombwell's Menagerie where, despite its size, it regularly hauled three trailers. It is a compound engine and similar to the bigger showmans engines in many respects but is not so extensively decorated. The three-speed

gears can be seen just above the rear wheel.

66 Burrell showmans road locomotive No. 3886, built 1920, XF 8162, *Lord Lascelles*

This is an example of the largest Burrell showmans engines and is commonly known as the 'scenic' type. It will be noticed that in addition to the big dynamo mounted in front of the chimney there is a second smaller one mounted on a stand between the chimney and the cylinder block. This dynamo was used to increase the power available, extra proving a necessity for starting the large fairground machines when fully loaded. A belt drive was taken from the offside of the main dynamo but in this view the extra pulley had still to be fitted. Note the gauges and switchboard by the front dynamo and the heat protection plate in front of the chimney. Electric lighting is fitted to this engine, the current being supplied by a steam-driven generator mounted on the nearside belly tank (not visible). Once used by the Gray family on the London area fairs, this engine has been driven by its intrepid crew all over England in preservation and has even ventured to Eire and Holland.

67 Burrell showmans road locomotive No. 3909, built 1922, NR 965, *Winston Churchill*

The showmans engine really comes to life when generating after dark and this view captures some of the atmosphere created. The engine is an 8-n.h.p. scenic-type double-crank compound similar to that in Plate 66 but viewed from the offside rear corner. Most interesting is the rear of the tender which is extended up to the canopy to form the strong base of a crane which could be used for lifting around the heavier pieces of the fairground operators' tackle. The winding rope on the nearside rear wheel was used to work the crane jib which pivoted in the tender drawbar bracket where in this view the drawbar pin may be seen. The vertical handwheel is the handbrake operating wheel which draws a wood block onto the inner rim of the rear wheel and by its side is the operating lever from the water injector to feed the boiler. Above the rear wheel is the road gear operating lever whilst up under the canopy the governor and safety-valve extension tubes can be picked out as well as the drive belt to the second or 'excitor' dynamo.

68 Burrell showmans road locomotive No. 3938, built 1922, XL 9086 *Quo Vadis*

A magnificent restoration to show condition has been carried out on this 8-n.h.p., double-crank compound, scenic-type showmans engine which was built originally for Wilsons of London. The decoration and lining out of the paintwork to Burrell's standard livery for these engines is first class with much gold leaf work included. Note the very wide rear wheels and typical maker's design of the chimney cap. Engines of this type frequently hauled loads of 50 tons or more hundreds of miles, averaging 12 miles an hour, as well as working generating on arrival.

69 Burrell showmans road locomotive No. 3979, built 1924, YA 9138, *Earl Haig*

A later model of the 7-n.h.p. double-crank compound showmans engine which worked in the West Country with Simonds & Cook. At the time this picture was taken it was generating power and has had the extension chimney erected to carry away the smoke. The big canopy is of the easily recognised Burrell design which gives a good deal of protection to the crew and the engine. Some of the decorative parts are chromed on this engine and this became more and more common as time progressed with fully-

chromed engines being built in the early 'thirties (Plate 76).

70 Foster showmans road locomotive No. 14502, built 1921, XC 9862, *Victory*

The Foster company did not build a great number of showmans engines and this is a typical example of their product. It was operated by Messrs Bird in the London area up to 1940 and then lay out of use until 1960 when restoration started and was nearing completion when this view was taken on its first outing in 1968. The engine is a 7-n.h.p. compound, and comparison with other Foster engines' pictures will point out several characteristics of the make. Special fittings for showmans use are the dynamo bracket which is bolted to the smokebox and has an especially distinctive side design and the canopy with its rounded shape to the cross members. At this time the twisted brass support decorations had still to be fitted.

71 Foster showmans road locomotive No. 14562, built 1932, AAU 370, *Success*

This was one of the last showmans engines built, not entering service until 1934, and is the only one to carry a three-letter registration plate. It was operated by Hibbles & Mellor in the East Midlands. The engine is one of the largest size normally used in this country, being a 10-n.h.p. compound machine. The typical Foster canopy and dynamo support bracket will be noted with the square nameplate across the front. Note also the tank motif on the maker's smokebox nameplate (see Plate 22). The engine is generating power for its owner's fairground organ standing alongside.

72 Fowler showmans engine No. 11799, built 1909, HO 5609, *Victory*

This is a most unusual and interesting engine. Originally it was built as a 5-

n.h.p. haulage tractor for the War Office, the cylinder arrangement being a three-cylinder compound. The extra third cylinder was fitted in front of the high-ing a necessity for starting the large pressure cylinder and shared its piston rod – steam from the high-pressure cylinder was, after use, passed equally to the orthodoxly positioned low-pressure cylinder and to the third cylinder which was of similar dimensions. It was suggested that the system equalised effort and made more economical use of the steam but the idea was not taken further and the engines were later converted to the more conventional compound arrangement. Almost all the working parts of this engine are enclosed, which is also a rare thing. In 1919 the engine was bought by a showman, J. Noyce, and converted for his use by addition of the dynamo and bracket and the full canopy. The engine is now the only one of its type in existence. though several other conventional former War Department engines later used by showmen still exist.

73 Fowler showmans road locomotive No. 14425, built 1916, DP 4418, *Carry On*

This is a Fowler Big Lion-type engine of 10 n.h.p., a double-crank compound with three-speed gearing. It is of especial interest as after use with Cadonas of Glasgow and McGiverns in Eire this was the last of these engines to be used by a showman in everyday use. It retired in 1959. The view shows the engine in a typical setting generating for the rides through its 300-amps, 110-volt dynamo at the Stratford-upon-Avon Steam Fair in 1970. Note the extension chimney fitted and a good pile of steam coal just to hand. The dynamo bracket appears to be of Foster design but typical Fowler motion covers and cylinder block show its true parentage. Note the offside steersman's position which makes kerb following a very difficult task with engines

of this type which have very restricted forward visibility.

74 Fowler showmans road locomotive No. 15653, built 1920, CU 978, *Renown*

Renown was one of a pair of identical engines supplied to J. Murphy of Gateshead to transport his scenic railway ride. This rear view of the 7-n.h.p. compound engine shows the base pole of the special 'Feast' crane fitted to handle the heavy parts of the ride. This crane had a jib pole which pivoted at the base of the fitted pole on the engine and was worked rather like a ship's derrick using the wire rope carried on the engine's nearside rear wheel. The guide rollers and wheels can be easily seen. The engine is a very good example of a Fowler showmans engine with the unusual blue livery a most distinctive feature.

75 Fowler showmans road locomotive No. 15657, built 1920, FX 6661, *Iron Maiden*

This is the famous showmans engine used in the film 'The Iron Maiden'. It is a 7-n.h.p. compound originally built as a normal road locomotive but rebuilt by Fowlers in 1932 to its present form when it acquired the name *Kitchener*. The distinctive Fowler items, such as the cylinder block, flywheel etc., will be noted and, as may be expected in a manufacturer's conversion, the dynamo bracket is formed as part of the smokebox plate. Another feature of Fowler engines is the long (compared with, say, a Burrell) footplate with a much easier access way for the driver to the rear of the back wheel. Fowler engines were also popularly reckoned to be the faster on a long journey but this depended greatly on the driver's skill.

76 and 77 Fowler showmans road locomotive No. 20223, built 1934, EU 5313, *Supreme*

Considered by many to be the finest

showmans engine ever built this Fowler Class B6, 10-n.h.p. compound was the last of the type built by this firm. The engine was built to the order of Mrs Deakin of South Wales with instructions to make it the finest on the road, but its actual working life was only six years on the fairgrounds. Early in the Second World War it was cut down to a road engine and worked on heavy haulage in the Glasgow area until retired about 1947. The subsequent restoration has taken many years but the original specification has been followed to produce what is possibly the finest restored traction engine in the world. The chromed decoration is as original and it will be noted that even the chimney cap is plated. The engine is seen in a fairground setting at the 1970 Blandford Steam Working.

78 Aveling & Porter tractor No. 11480, built 1926

This is a single-cylinder, piston-valve version of the popular 5-ton Aveling & Porter light tractor. In this view the features of an engine designed for road use can be seen, such as the motion side plates to hide the moving parts. The wheels are of the built-up traction engine type in contrast with the cast versions seen on the tractor in Plate 79. Note also the mud or dust covers over the transmission gears.

79 Aveling & Porter tractor No. 11486, built 1926, KM 7100, *Nellie*

A typical light tractor of a type built in large numbers by Aveling & Porter. The engine is a piston-valve compound and probably has two-speed gears (compare with Plate 78). The cast rear wheels are a design used almost exclusively by Aveling & Porter on tractors whilst the front axle appears to be a replacement type. Note the extra belly water tanks under the boiler and enclosed worm steering gear.

80 Burrell 4-n.h.p. tractor No. 3191, built 1910, VLJ 346, *Furious*

This 5-ton tractor started life as a War Department crane engine later passing into showmans use and general haulage. It is a compound engine with several Burrell features in the cylinder block design, flywheel shape, smokebox door nameplates and chimney cap. These were a very popular make built in large numbers. Note the cylinder exhaust pipe running into the side of the smokebox.

81 Foster tractor No. 14514, built 1922, CA 8534, *Duke of Wellington*

These 5-n.h.p., 5-ton tractors were known as the Wellington type; hence the engine's name and the portrait on the belly tank of this example. It is a typical light tractor with all the usual features found on these engines but to the Foster style. Of note is the First World War tank motif on the bottom of the smokebox round nameplate commemorating Foster's work in building the first of these vehicles.

82 Fowler tractor No. 15632, built 1920, SP 8063, *Tiger*

This T3-type engine was known as the Tiger type and was, in most respects, a scaled down version of Fowler's road engines. It is a two-speed, compound machine. Details of note are the slightly dished flywheel design, the brass covers to the cylinder block and canopy and chimney cap designs. The wood block flywheel brake may be seen just above the belly tank.

83 Garrett tractor No. 33986, built 1920, BJ 5601, *Victor*

One of the most successful light tractors was the Garrett 4-n.h.p. compound of the type seen in this view. A typical tractor design in every way, Garrett features are the big 'G' motif on the smokebox, the flywheel design with oval slots around the inner rim and the funnel and canopy designs. Quite large belly tanks are fitted and brass extension tubes from the safety valves to carry excess steam away over the roof. As on most tractors, strip rubber bolted-on tyres are fitted.

84 Marshall tractor No. 73900, built 1920, AH 823

This Marshall 5-ton tractor is a compound engine fitted with the maker's radial valve gear instead of the almost universal Stephenson link motion gear on traction engines. It is believed to be one of two tractors surviving with this arrangement. The restoration of this engine is to the appearance in which it was exhibited at the 1920 Smithfield Show. Note the solid, small disc-type flywheel and smokebox diameter smaller than the boiler barrel; also the wood supports to the canopy. A size comparison can be made with the 7-n.h.p. road locomotive alongside.

85 McLaren tractor No. 1837, built 1936, AAM 801, *Bluebell*

One of the youngest steam engines in Britain and possibly the last steam tractor to be built; very few engines were allocated three letter registrations, the issue of which commenced in 1933. All the usual tractor features are present on the 4-n.h.p. compound engine and the small disc-type flywheel is of note. It is also probable that this was the last steam engine built for home use by McLarens as the company was absorbed by Fowlers soon after.

86 Ransomes, Sims & Jefferies tractor No. 39127, built 1928, PN 1903, *General Wolfe*

The Ransomes version of the 5-ton tractor is shown by means of this very nice example. A compound cylindered engine with the maker's initials on the cover plate to the cylinders and a useful three-quarter-length canopy to protect both crew and engine. The wheels are still on

strakes in the form in which these light tractors were supplied when new, but over the years nearly all have been fitted with rubber tyres.

87 Robey tractor No. 37657, built 1918, AP 9341, *The Guv'nor*

The Robey version of the popular 5-ton, 4-n.h.p. tractor. It is a compound engine with a large cylinder block and heavy, dished flywheel. The almost flat smoke-box door is a feature of this make. A pan on the front axle is unusual on tractors. This example went new to the War Department but saw later use on a Sussex estate.

88 Ruston & Proctor tractor No. 52573, built 1918, TF 8240, *Lincoln Imp*

Ruston's version of the 5-ton tractor with a very long overall canopy giving a rather tall and top-heavy appearance to the engine. The front axle has a very long perch bracket which has to be supported by a stay back to the firebox front. Only two of these tractors are known to survive today.

89 Tasker tractor No. 1296, built 1903, BY 160, *The Horse's Friend*

One of the most famous steam engines in Britain this small 4-n.h.p., 3-ton tractor was given to the R.S.P.C.A. and used to assist the dray horses climbing the hills around the Crystal Palace area of London. The engine is a single-cylinder, three-shaft, class A1 machine very similar to the one shown in Plate 90. Note the hand rear-wheel brake on the right side of the driver's footplate. The engine is seen at a Clapham Transport Museum Open Day sitting in its transporter.

90 Tasker tractor No. 1309, built 1904, DV 9883

This engine is a single-cylinder ($5\frac{1}{4}'' \times 9''$) machine with slide valves and has just visible beside the rear wheel a gear-driven water feed pump which is an unusual fitting. It was built as a tractor, converted to a roller as many light engines were and has only recently been re-converted using non-standard cast front wheels. The use of old tractor tyre rubber on the rear wheels is also a new feature which has appeared on several engines recently with apparent success in use despite the strange appearance. The canopy of this engine is to a distinctive Tasker design.

91 Wallis & Steevens tractor No. unknown, built 1903, GRX 400, *Goliath*

This is an example of one of the smallest road tractor designs built in any number and weighs only around 3 tons. There is a single-cylinder and despite the small size all the usual tractor fittings. A conversion of one of these engines may be seen illustrated in Plate 131.

92 Wallis & Steevens tractor No. 7641, built 1921, BW 4658, *Surprise*

This is a 5-ton, 4-n.h.p. compound tractor showing the smokebox 'Wallis Patent Motor' badge found on many of the Wallis & Steevens light engines. Note the brass extension pipes to the safety valves to carry away the steam from under the canopy and the plain design Wallis chimney cap. Smooth running and long life for the moving parts were ensured on these engines by enclosing most of them in an oil bath.

93 Wallis & Steevens tractor No. 7881, built 1927, PR 8420, *Morning Star*

A compact road tractor of unusual design with the very small front wheels producing a heavy appearance to the engine. It is a two-speed compound very strongly built and well equipped. The full length canopy, large belly tanks, big cylinder block and the almost complete conceal-

ment of the motion work are features of note.

94 Aveling & Porter showmans tractor No. 7612, built 1912, F 5218, *May Queen*

This 4-n.h.p. double-crank compound tractor is a conversion from a haulage tractor and has therefore the correct design wheels sometimes absent on conversions. Note the thin spokes to the front wheels and the heavy Y section spoke cast wheels at the rear. The prancing horse on the smokebox door was this maker's trade mark. This was a popular tractor and many found their way onto the fairgrounds in the 'thirties.

95 Aveling & Porter showmans tractor No. 7899, built 1913, *Southern Queen*

Hardly recognisable as a conversion from a roller is this 4-n.h.p. double-crank compound showmans tractor. Tractor wheels have replaced the rolls and a new smokebox incorporating the dynamo bracket fitted. The belly tanks are smaller than usual on a tractor whilst just in front of these note the enclosed steering gear found on many Avelings. The decoration of the engine is reminiscent of the late Victorian showmans engines when it was popular to cover the engines in painted designs of this style.

96 Burrell showmans tractor No. 3894, built 1921, NX 947, *Saint Brannock*

This is a 6-n.h.p. double-crank compound engine which worked around Devon on haulage before preservation days. It has been converted to the showmans style by the addition of the dynamo, overall canopy, brass fittings etc., but the basic road engine can still be clearly seen. Conversions of this nature were frequently carried out by showmen who either did not require or could not afford the very large, purpose-built engines. The Burrell cylinder block and chimney are easy identification points.

97 Foster showmans tractor No. 13036, built 1913, FE 1079, *Pride of Acrise*

A very nice conversion of a Foster 4-n.h.p. double-crank compound tractor to showmans style to accompany its owner's fairground organ which it is seen here towing away from a rally field. The twin decorated caps of the cylinders show well and extra decoration has been applied to the motion covers and belly tanks. The overall canopy is built in the Foster style with an arched front design.

98 Fowler showmans tractor No. 21221, built 1937, CVO 734, *Forest Queen*

Fowlers built several small showmans tractors new but this one is a clever conversion from a 6-ton road roller carried out in recent times. The engine is a neat 4-n.h.p. compound which has been fitted with tractor wheels, a smokebox extension and the usual dynamo and brass fittings associated with a showmans engine. A full length canopy of correct shape completes this careful conversion. Note the rectangular Fowler nameplate of a type found on many of the later rollers of this make.

99 Garrett showmans tractor No. 31193, built 1913, BJ 1659, *Henrietta*

An example of the very popular Garrett 4-n.h.p. double-crank compound tractor fitted in preservation days with showmans fittings. These tractors were well finished – note the neat coverings to the gears by the rear wheel and general tidy arrangement of the various parts of the engine. Although no nameplate is visible to read the identity of the maker the cylinder block shape and chimney design are characteristic features. The coiled suction hose on the belly tank is used to lift water

from ponds or rivers into the tanks when out on the road.

100 Robey showmans tractor No. 41492, built 1923, FE 5736

Only a handful of Robey's tractors survive. A 4-n.h.p. compound, this engine was built for the R.A.S.C. and later passed into general haulage work before its conversion to the present form in preservation. The conversion was completed to Robey's specification for showmans tractors, and so is very similar to those actually built by the firm for this use. The large-diameter Robey boiler with a flat smokebox door is visible and a solid flywheel is fitted. The very strong wheels are of note as the small number of spokes in the rear wheels has made thicker than average-size spokes necessary.

101 Tasker showmans tractor No. 1822, built 1920, NO 2930, *Little Jim II*

This is the only Tasker showmans engine surviving. It was first used for haulage and then converted by Smarts into its present style. The engine is a 4-n.h.p. compound, three-shaft tractor of the usual Tasker design – note the neat enclosure of the gears and very prominent brass maker's plate on the motion covers. The small dynamo is built on an extension in front of the chimney complete with a small switchboard whilst the whole engine is covered by a neat canopy supported on brass uprights.

102 Armstrong-Whitworth 10-ton road roller No. 10R19, built 1923, FJ 2795

Sir W. G. Armstrong-Whitworth & Co. Ltd were the last firm to start building steam engines in Britain and only built about 50 in all. This engine is a piston-valve compound of the distinctive design built by this firm of which one of the main features is the front roll head incorporating the tool box. Another feature of note is the plate- instead of spoke-supported rolls. Steel casting were used throughout the construction of the roller giving it an actual weight in full working order of around 15 tons. This one is painted in the blue of Exeter Corporation its original owner but the standard livery was unrelieved buff-yellow.

103 Aveling & Porter 10-ton road roller No. 2941, built 1892, AL 9463

Several pre-1900 rollers still exist, having worked very long and useful lives. This example is a 10-tonner which has always been a popular size and shows the main features of a roller. The massive two-part front roll and smooth rear rolls like traction engine wheels without strakes are the most common wheel design. The engine itself is similar to a traction engine and some types were convertible from one form to the other in a very short time. Aveling & Porter, trade mark the rampant horse of Kent, were the largest British builders of rollers.

104 Aveling & Porter 10-ton roller No. 6378, built 1907, PR 9581

A double-crank compound engine with slide valves showing some of the features found on most Aveling rollers. The cab roof design is distinctive whilst the boiler feed pump on the boiler side operated by an eccentric on the crankshaft was almost universal. On the tender rear offside is the scarifier used to rip up the old road surface prior to work being carried out. It is mounted firmly to the tender plates and by a link to the rear axle which permits the section of the scarifier in which the tines (iron prongs) are fitted to be lowered into the surface by means of the hand wheel visible on its side.

105 Aveling & Porter 12-ton roller No. 6893, built 1909, KK 9032

An excellent example of the large single-cylinder rollers popular in the early years of this century, this engine is still used occasionally by its owner in his business. The massive casting to support the front rolls forms the chimney base as well and has a slot at the front end to take the upper part of the front fork casting. This allows, by its loose fit, the front roll assembly to turn and rock from side to side when traversing uneven surfaces. The boiler feed valve and inspection hole can be seen on the boiler barrel and the early design of the Aveling & Porter nameplate on the cylinder block side. The reversing lever and handbrake wheel can be seen just above the rear roll.

106 Aveling & Porter 8-ton road roller No. 9108, built 1920, BP 6711

A type K.N.D. 4-n.h.p. compound, slide-valve engine built in the 'convertible' form which was especially popular with local authorities as it permitted all the year round and varied use of the engine. In between the chimney and the front roll support a bolted joint can be seen which permitted the front assembly to be removed and replaced with normal traction engine front axle and wheels. Exchanging the rear rolls for ordinary traction engine rear wheels produced a light tractor which could be used for normal haulage work. It will be noted that this engine has belly tanks, as on many tractors (see Plate 78 & 79). The conversion could easily be carried out in a morning's work.

107 Aveling & Porter 10-ton roller No. 10594, built 1923, YA 6375

The very distinctive cylinder block of the piston-valve compound engine can be seen clearly on this powerful roller. The large, although thin, solid flywheel and very high perch bracket to support the front rolls and chimney shape are also easily recognised Aveling features. Rollers of this type were introduced shortly after the First World War and were amongst the first built by the company on standard jigs to give the maximum standardisation of parts.

108 Aveling & Porter 8-ton roller No. 11675, built 1926, RK 8041

This is an example of the single-cylinder, piston-valve design produced in quite large numbers in the 'twenties. The distinctive shape of the cylinder block may be seen with the red painted automatic lubricator found on virtually all engines mounted just above it. Note also the spark arrester on the chimney – a feature often absent on preserved engines – and the reinforcement of the cast-iron front fork by a plate possibly fitted to give extra support following the discovery of cracks in the original casting.

109 Aveling & Porter 10-ton roller No. 14070, built 1930, VN 2094

Probably the ultimate in steam roller design the type A.D. was introduced in 1930 with several improvements over previous models and an interesting design. Not a great number were built, as the diesel roller was improving rapidly and must have hit sales. The slide-valve compound engine was thought by many to be the most economical and efficient for roller work and repair saving features such as totally enclosed steering gear and gearing within the hornplates were incorporated. The cab roof design, constructed entirely of metal, is the Aveling & Porter standard design.

110 Aveling & Barford 10-ton roller No. AC606, built 1946, DTM 538

This roller shows the final development of the British steam roller, being one of the few built for use in this country after the 1939–1945 war. The actual construction was carried out by a branch of Vickers-Armstrong at Newcastle but to

designs used by Aveling Barford in the 1937–1939 period, which were based on the earlier Ruston & Hornsby designs. Rustons had been absorbed by the firm in 1932. The engine is a piston-valve type and the flywheel is a distinctive feature. Aveling front end design was used as well as several other minor parts.

Eddison Plant Ltd who own this roller in preservation, were once the largest steam road-rolling contracting company in the country, the distinctive design of canopy and name being a familiar sight wherever road works were being carried out.

111 Babcock & Wilcox 6-ton roller No. 95/4009, built 1926, YB 7976, *Toby*

Babcock & Wilcox absorbed the long-established engine builders of Clayton and Shuttleworth in 1924 and shortly afterwards produced a few rollers under the new name but of general C & S design. The distinguishing marks are the nameplates, whilst the canopy design and front badge show its parentage. This is a single-cylinder engine of conventional design with the heavy, roller-type, solid flywheel. Note also the rear wheel spokes cast into the rim.

112 Burrell 8-ton roller No. 4018, built 1925, PR 4449, *Thomas Hardy*

An unusual double-crank compound roller which, although an 8-tonner, is fitted with the front rolls usually used on the 10-ton version thus requiring a swan-neck style of front roll support to accommodate the bigger front roll. This can be seen, carrying the script style of maker's name fitted to most Burrell rollers, rising up in front of the chimney to get the clearance. Rollers of this make are not as common as their other types of engine and this example has just been totally rebuilt after 10 years out of use.

113 **Burrell 14-ton roller No. 4070, built 1927, WW 2181**
This was one of the last rollers built by Burrells and is a very large machine compared to the average British roller. It is a single-cylinder, slide-valve machine of the distinctive Burrell design in such places as the cylinder block, flywheel, chimney and front roll support. The size of the roller can be judged against the car standing alongside.

114 **Clayton & Shuttleworth 10-ton roller No. 48946, built 1924, YA 9576**
This was one of the last engines built by Clayton & Shuttleworth the firm being taken over by Babcock & Wilcox shortly after (see Plate 111 for an example and comparison). This is the larger 10-ton single-cylinder machine the finer points of which are shown well in this excellently restored example. The tidy appearance is complete even to the fire irons on their hook at the rear of the canopy.

115 **Fowler/Allen 10-ton roller No. 8111, built 1905, BW 4798**
John Allen & Sons of Oxford were a firm connected with contracting and engine repairs who had very strong connections with John Fowler of Leeds, the builders of ploughing engines. This engine was one of several built up by Allens using parts supplied by Fowlers and is numbered in their series; but it will be noted that it carries the Allen badge on the front roll support. The high bracket is common on heavier, early engines as is the single-cylinder and big-flywheel arrangement. Note the unusual light design of the front fork and the curved Fowler design motion covers.

116 **Fowler 10-ton roller No. 16100, built 1924, FF 1779, *Gloria***
A powerful road roller which spent its working life in North Wales until it retired in 1964. The rather long ap-

pearance is typical of many larger Fowler rollers with the front roll placed well to the fore, enabling the crew to have excellent access to the smokebox for cleaning it and the tubes. It is a single-cylinder engine and carries the maker's design of cab roof. Note the script maker's name fitted to many rollers of this make and the scarifier on the rear of the tender.

117 **Fowler 6-ton roller No. 19032, built 1930, FLR 257, *Doris***
Originally this roller was exported to Java where it spent the first eight years of its working life before returning to work in the Thames Valley area. It has several items not found on home models, including gauges and nameplates etc. giving information and dimensions in metric measurements. The engine is a single-cylinder very similar in many respects to the light tractors built by the firm. Note the later type of maker's nameplate at the front and typical chimney design.

118 **Fowler 10-ton roller No. 18075, built 1930, CV 1662, *Britannia***
A single-cylinder machine with the usual Fowler features such as the slightly dished shape of the heavy flywheel. Note the slot in the front roll supporting head to permit movement of the front roll assembly over uneven surfaces. From their thickness it appears that the rear rolls have seen little use since their last replating.

119 **Green 8-ton roller No. 1968, built 1914, TA 2431**
The Green company of Leeds did not build many engines and all that exist today are rollers. This single-cylinder engine was built for the War Department and probably served during the First World War on the Continent. Like many others it was sold after the war and was bought by Devon County Council who still operate it as Fleet No. 111. It is a small, neat machine with an unusual style of front roll support to distinguish it

from other makes. Note also the canvas side screens rolled up around the canopy which only need untying to drop down to protect the engine overnight.

120 Mann roller No. 1145, built 1915, KM 514, *Miss Mann*

A most interesting and unusual roller based on the Mann steam cart design (see Plate 158). It was intended for use as a light roller in maintaining paths and drives and when built carried a small body to hold asphalt ready for use – its place has now been taken by an additional water tank. At the front the usual lorry-type front wheels have been replaced by small rolls whilst at the rear there is a full-width large roll. A chain drive is taken down the near side of the engine to the rear roll. This is one of the very few rollers which are mounted on springs on *all* rolls, the more usual practice being no springs at all.

121 Marshall 12-ton roller No. 68955, built 1916, TA 212

This engine was part of the large fleet once owned by Devon County Council of which a few still remain in use. It is still in its previous owners' livery and has the typical appearance of a working roller. A double-crank compound engine, it was used for a time as a 5-n.h.p. tractor but was later fitted with the distinctive Marshall front roll support and small roll. An unusual feature is the use of alloy securing bands around the boiler lagging plates.

122 Marshall 8-ton roller No. 79669, built 1925, PX 2690, *Joan*

Still with its original owners and in daily use throughout 1970 on the roads of West Sussex was this single-cylinder Marshall roller. It is seen here working on trench re-instatement work. Points of interest are the rear wheel design which is found on many Marshalls, the large rounded front roll support, the decorative 'M' on

the cylinder end and the small heavy flywheel. Note the canvas screen arranged to give the driver some protection from a cold wind when this view was taken on a winter's day.

123 Marshall 10-ton roller No. 81095, built 1926, RF 1834, *Bordon Queen*

A larger version of the single-cylinder roller shown on Plate 122 with similar features typical of most rollers of this make. The rounded front roll support cap is however missing on this example. It will be noted that most rollers have three-quarter-length canopies which are fitted to protect the motion work as well as the driver and are very necessary when the engine is left out at the roadside during a job. Scrapers to remove any road metal caught on the rolls are normally fitted and one can be seen at the front side of the rear roll in this view.

124 Marshall 12-ton roller No. 88096, built 1937, DAF 560

An example of the last type of roller built by Marshalls and a heavy version of the model. Known as the S type this engine is a piston-valve compound with the maker's radial valve gear, which has a single eccentric for each cylinder instead of the usual double-link motion. Unfortunately this is hidden against the dirt and dust of the road behind the motion covers. The bold maker's name across the front of the cylinder block is a most distinctive feature. A scarifier is fitted at the rear and the trade mark Brittania above the front roll.

125 Robey 8-ton roller No. 42216, built 1925, FE 6672

The Robey company built some interesting rollers of unusual designs, although this is one of their conventional machines. The engine is a double-crank compound, very well enclosed and with the drive gears protected by substantial covers. There is a very distinctive front roll support bracket of a rounded design whilst the front roll itself is very thick at its rolling surface, suggesting it has not seen a great deal of use. Note the scarifier at the rear. When this view was taken an overhaul was not fully completed so the lack of lagging on the boiler shows the riveted construction of the boiler joints.

126 Robey 4-ton tandem roller No. 42520, built 1925, *Barkis*

This unusual-looking machine was one of a quite popular lighter roller built by Robeys in tandem form. Very few machines of this type exist today and none of similar machines built by other makers. Most unusual for a steam roller is the use of a chassis which can be seen running the length of the vehicle. Inside this is set one of the 'pistol'-shape boilers built by Robeys (see also on Robey wagons), the round firebox of which can be seen in the centre. The engine, mounted over the boiler, is a double-crank compound with a chain drive to the rear roll. Note the steering by means of a quadrant above the front roll and the cast segments of the four piece front roll itself. The rear roll is full width and in some cases could be water-ballasted for extra weight. Additional water for the boiler is carried in the tank slung underneath the chassis and overall cover is given by the distinctive Robey style of roof. This engine forms part of the fascinating working collection at Bressingham Hall, Norfolk, which is open to the public on most summer Sundays.

127 Robey tri-tandem roller No. 45655, built 1930, VL 2773

A roller which always interests the crowds when it appears at rallies! Basically it is similar to the tandem version shown in Plate 126 but it was modified during its working life by the addition of a second rear roll. The additional chassis members and supporting brackets can be seen along the near side and there is a second chain drive linking the two rear rolls. This most interesting machine spent the last few months of its working life helping prepare the M1 motorway.

128 Ruston & Hornsby 10-ton roller No. 115124, built 1923, XM 6374, *Veronica*

A rare make of steam roller. The engine is a single-cylinder machine with a very square block and unusual curved motion covers. Note the typical heavy, large-diameter solid flywheel, much favoured on rollers to give smooth running, and the chain-steering roller fitted to the front of the firebox and looking like a piece of candy. This shape helps wind the chain on and off smoothly. The front fork has been plated and possibly suffers from hair-line cracks following years of vibration on the unsprung front roll.

129 Tasker 6-ton convertible roller No. 1409, built 1909, AA 2299

Although looking basically similar to the roller shown on Plate 130, this engine has several interesting differences. It is a compound with overtype, inclined valves used on earlier engines in the main – comparison of the two cylinder blocks will show the differences. As a convertible engine the front roll support is bolted to the smokebox for easy removal. The conversion to its present form from an ordinary tractor was carried out by Taskers in 1930 and as an experiment a five-section, cast-iron front roll was fitted. Note the 'Little Giant' nameplate, which is an item fitted to all the small Tasker engines, and the canopy design which is an easily distinguished shape.

130 **Tasker 6-ton roller No. 1902, built 1923, KL 9885**

Like many light rollers this one started life as a haulage tractor. Of the Class B2 type, it is a compound engine with the cylinders mounted centrally and the valve chests on either side. An unusual feature is a double-high regulator system if required and a balanced crankshaft: both items no doubt inherited from its tractor days together with the belly tanks and rear springs. Note the Tasker style flywheel with a wide rim on the outside edge.

131 **Wallis & Steevens 5-ton roller No. 2656, built 1903, HO 5834, *Little Olga***

One of the smallest engines in Great Britain, this was originally a tractor (see Plate 91) but was converted in 1920 to a roller by addition of the front roll and replacement of the rear wheels. Bolting on the front roll support to the smokebox was the usual practice on Wallis & Steevens engines. The engine is a single-cylinder originally rated at 3 n.h.p. By comparison, standing next to the Wallis in this view is Burrell roller No. 3991, an 8-tonner which looks quite massive. Burrell rollers are not common and this is a good example of their single-cylinder model. Note the script-style maker's name and disc flywheel. The disc behind the registration plate is the chimney cover for overnight use.

132 **Wallis & Steevens 10-ton roller No. 7799, built 1924, HO 6354, *Daisy May***

A typical, conventionally designed Wallis & Steevens roller. This one is a compound engine, as is indicated by the large cylinder block and has a short canopy, which is not usual practice on rollers. The front roll support is bolted to the smokebox which is normal on engines of this make, giving the appearance of being converted. The roll design is unusual,

being a large version of the types fitted to the 'Advance' rollers.

133 **Wallis & Steevens 'Advance' 8-ton roller No. 7962, built 1928, OT 8117, *Smokey***

The Advance road roller, of which this is a fine example, was developed in the early 'twenties to cope with the new, finer, road materials such as asphalt then coming into use. This engine is a double high-pressure cylinder unit which needs virtually no flywheel and can be reversed almost without any pause – a great advantage if no depressions are to be left in a soft road surface. The wide rolls give a low pressure per unit of surface covered which is also of advantage. The steering is very positive, being worked by a vertical wheel on the driver's platform via a geared quadrant mounted directly above the front roll. Belly water tanks are fitted and coal bunkers on each side of the driver's platform, which is approached from the rear. This actual roller is very active in retirement, travelling several hundreds of miles each year under its own steam to rally events.

134 **Wallis & Steevens 'Advance' roller No. 8100, built 1934, BAA 432, *Pride of the Hills***

The Advance-type roller was built in three sizes – 6-, 8- and 10-ton, of which the majority, like this one, were 8-tonners. The engine's main specifications are similar to that on Plate 133 but a difference is that this was one of three built with full-width belly tanks. Also, as this was one of the last built, the later style of Advance badge on the front is the type better known on diesel rollers. The side motion cover is off, allowing one to see the connecting rod from one of the cylinders joining the crankshaft by a small disc crank. Note also the corrugated iron roof which was standard on all the Advance rollers.

135 **Foden steam wagon No. 10530,
built 1921, TA 1216,**
Pride of the West

This is an example of the very successful
Foden overtype steam wagon in its first
full production form and is the type which
was responsible for the strong following
of Fodens by many operators. Some of
the early examples built in the first few
years of this century had outside frame
chassis but these soon gave way to the
design depicted, of which this is a very
late example. The front end of the
locomotive-type boiler can be clearly
seen with the compound cylinder block
just behind the chimney. The flywheel is
next to the driver's position with the
steering wheel just below. The chassis
frame runs from the front end straight
through to the rear supporting the entire
wagon except for the front axle, which is
fastened traction-engine-style to the
smokebox. On these wagons the crew
space is very cramped, with about two
feet between the firebox and the back of
the cab. Firing the engine is not easy in
this space, especially as the coal supply is
usually under the body. The driver sits
outside the chassis in a rather precarious
position on the near side which makes a
journey in today's traffic a difficult task.

136 **Foden steam bus No. 11340,
built 1922, M 6341**

Steam buses were never very common,
the only really practical versions being
oil-fired machines which looked not
unlike the contemporary lorries. However some conversions of coal-fired steam
lorries were built and saw limited use with
most of the main manufacturers trying at
least one design. This particular vehicle
was built as a lorry and has had the bus
body fitted in preservation days but it is a
replica of one built by Fodens and used
by them for a time in the 'twenties (for
the transport of the famous brass band, it
is said!). The chassis is the wagon type
introduced in 1920 with improvements on

the earlier design. Note the exposed chain
drive to the rear wheels and the band
hand brake on the rear axle.

137 **Foden wagon No. 13008, built
1928, UR 1328,** *Little Alice*

A rare example of a multiple-axle Foden
wagon which is possibly unique today.
Basically, the engine is the same as the
four-wheelers except for the rear bogie
on which all wheels are driven by means
of a connecting chain between the axles.
In this view the locomotive-type boiler
is easily noticed, the base of the firebox
appearing just behind the front wheels.
The cab is an intermediate stage design
with an open front and sides but with the
crew space improved and right-hand
steering fitted.

This wagon was once a tar carrier but
has since been rebuilt as a tractor with a
section of the chassis between the axles
removed to shorten the length. The new
all-steel body consists of water tanks and
coal storage, allowing long journeys to be
made without water stops.

138 **Foden wagon No. 13716, built
1930, RP 9208,** *Peg O' My Heart*

This 6-ton, three-way tipping wagon is
an excellent example of the later Foden
wagons and was restored by the well-
known steam enthusiast, Jack Hampshire,
who is seen checking that all is well. The
main differences to the earlier wagons are
the improvements to the cab, which is
nearly fully enclosed and much more
spacious, and the mechanical improvements to the engine motion. The driving
position is on the off side and all controls
fall easily to hand. The chain drive to the
rear axle is retained and on this example
the water tank underneath and suction
lifter hose are visible. In order to tip the
body use is made of the reserve water to
operate an hydraulic hoist mounted
centrally under the wagon body, the
pump being driven off the engine. Tippers
of this kind were much used by local

authorities and this particular one started life with the Northamptonshire County Council.

139 Foden timber tractor No. 13266, built 1928, VJ 1476, *Pride of Bucks*

An example of a special version of the Foden steam wagon for use on timber hauling on the road with pole trailers as well as for winching out felled trees and loading them on the trailers. The front end as far back as the driver's cab is not altered, but the rear end is modified, the rear axle being brought forward as far as the larger than usual rear wheels permit. These wheels are often fitted with extra spuds to obtain grip on muddy ground but this example has had rubber tyres fitted for road use. A winch driven from the wagon's engine is often mounted in the rear for hauling work and special spades fitted to the rear of the chassis to anchor the whole vehicle. These engines were very practical and popular machines, being designed for a specific job – the short wheelbase allowed manoeuvring in small spaces, the power winch ample pulling power and the basic wagon unit good performance when on the road with a load.

140 Foden tractors No. 12852, built 1928, RX 1719. No. 14078, built 1932, MJ 369, *Mighty Atom* and No. 13238, built 1929, UU 111, *Berkshire Belle*

This interesting view was taken at the 1966 Appleford Rally. It shows three different forms of Foden tractor.

No. 12852 on the left is in its original form with solid tyres all round but has had some weather protection fitted to the cab. No. 14078 is an example of the very last type of Foden overtype wagon, being the next to last built, and has pneumatic tyres on the front axle with solids still on the rear which, on this occasion, have been fitted with chains for grip on the

muddy surface. This too has an enclosed cab. No. 13238 on the right is a conversion from a 6-ton wagon which has been shortened in the chassis to make a tractor unit for hauling trailers on the road and was probably fitted at this same time with pneumatic tyres on all wheels.

141 Garrett 8-ton wagon No. 35465, built 1931, CV 5166

The 'QL' Garrett wagon was a most interesting design of undertype wagon which had one of the most advanced engines of its day. The boiler is a vertical, water-tube type working at 250 pounds per sq. inch pressure which is high for a steam road vehicle. Steam is supplied to a high speed duplex poppet-valve engine which featured a balanced crankshaft mounted under the chassis just to the rear of the cab. The drive from this engine is taken via a geared drive and differential in unit with the engine and then by chains to the rear axle. Ackermann steering is fitted and all the road wheels run on roller bearings. The virtually fully enclosed cab was a design dating from the mid-'twenties with its extensive glazing giving excellent weather protection as well as ample visibility. These were popular, fast wagons built in both four- and six-wheel versions, but only two survive to the present day of which this is the only one active at present. No body has yet been fitted and ballast weights are being carried but the mounting brackets for a side-tipping body may be seen on the extreme end of the chassis. Note the covers on the rear wheels giving them a solid appearance.

142 Robey 6-ton wagon No. 42657, built 1921, MY 319

This design of Robey wagon dates from 1918 and incorporates the maker's unusual 'pistol' type boiler, so named because of its shape (a similar boiler may be seen better in a roller shown in Plate 126). The firebox is circular in cross-section requiring no stays between the inner and outer shells – a distinct advantage in both construction and maintenance. The working pressure is 250 pounds per sq. inch. The engine itself is a compound with piston valves driving through a balanced crankshaft with final drive by chain to the rear axle. The brakes act on the rear-wheel inner tyre rims. The basic layout of the controls, water tanks etc. is similar to other overtypes.

It is believed that this is the sole example of this make of wagon now in existence.

143 Sentinel 'Standard' type wagon No. 1286, built 1916, AW 2964

The Sentinel wagon is the best known of the undertype wagons and one of the most successful wagons produced.

This example is one of the earliest survivors of the make and carries the first style of cab with an open front and sides. The vertical water-tube boiler can be seen mounted right at the front of the chassis behind the apron carrying the owner's name with the base of the firebox and ashpan showing well below this. The boiler supplies steam at 230 pounds per sq. inch to a totally enclosed duplex engine mounted below the chassis and to the rear of the driver's cab. A modern feature was the use of a camshaft to operate the poppet valves in the engine with the whole unit running in an oil bath – a far cry from the usual exposed motion of most contemporary engines. The drive to the rear axle is via chains in the normal fashion.

The owners of this wagon still (in 1970) operate a few similar vehicles in their steelworks, the very high temperatures precluding the use of motor transport.

144 Sentinel 'Super' wagon No. 5509, built 1924, PD 1701

Mechanically the wagon in this view is similar to that shown in Plate 145, but the side view allows additional features to be seen. The totally enclosed engine can be seen suspended underneath the chassis with the chain drive to the rear wheels. The cab is the standard Sentinel design and through the driver's door can be seen the steering column and control levers. Windscreens are fitted to this example, producing a reasonably weatherproof cab, and it will be noted the screens open to give additional ventilation. Behind the cab is the water tank which, beside providing the boiler water supply, is also used to operate the hydraulic hoist mounted in the centre of the chassis below the centre point of the body. An auxiliary pump on the engine pumps water into the hoist which, being mounted on a large ball bearing, can tip the body to either side or the rear depending on which pins are removed around the sides of the body. These pins may be seen on the underside of the body and on the chassis. The bucket hung beneath is below the injector, thus preventing any water leaking out onto the ground, creating mud and as a result causing the lorry to get stuck when it trys to move off. Note the narrow-section solid rubber tyres.

145 Sentinel 'Super' tractor No. 5558, built 1924, PD 1854

The Super type of Sentinel appeared in 1923 and followed the basic principles of its predecessors with a vertical boiler at the front and the under-chassis duplex engine mounted just behind the cab. It will be noted that the chimney is at the extreme front – i.e. to one side of the boiler – permitting a central firing chute which was said to give an even fire on the circular grate. The water-tube boiler has inclined tubes, which it was thought would be to a certain extent self-cleaning by vibration. A superheater coil is fitted at the top of the boiler just below the chimney. At the lower end the grate and ashpan are hinged and held in place by a simple clip which allows the fire to be dropped quickly in an emergency as well as facilitating cleaning – in this view the grate is in the down position. Drive to the rear wheels is by chains, the differential being housed in unit with the engine. This tractor is a conversion from a lorry for use in hauling trailers and the pneumatic tyres were also an addition during its working life.

146 Sentinel DG6 wagon No. 8213, built 1930, GF 8655

The DG series of Sentinels replaced the Super series in the late 'twenties with the number following the 'DG' showing the number of wheels fitted (note: twins at the rear count as one wheel). The main difference was in the larger duplex engine giving more power and working at a steam pressure of 275 pounds per sq. inch. The rear bogie was chain-driven with an additional connecting endless chain between the two axles to give double axle drive. This example is fitted with a tank body which must be very useful for water carrying today, although in the past many steam lorries were fitted with tanks for carrying tar, the tar being kept fluid by means of the boiler steam. Note the very strong girder chassis and the size of the steering box and steering arms which are certainly not of lightweight construction.

147 Sentinel DG4 wagon No. 7954, built 1929, PG 2414

This is another example of the DG series Sentinel wagon and reference may be made to Plate 146 for its mechanical details. The greater part of Sentinel production was of wagons of this general design and size where the undertype engine and compact vertical boiler enabled a good load space behind the cab to be provided. This gave a great advantage over the overtype wagons. Several wagons of this type were at work commercially up until the late nineteen-fifties.

148 Sentinel timber tractor No. 8777, built 1933, JB 1655, Old Bill

This is one of a number of special DG type Sentinels built as timber-winching tractors. The basic chassis is similar to the ordinary lorries and tractors and the cab, boiler and engine are of the type used in the DG series. It will be noticed that the tractor is built much higher than usual to give a good ground clearance and to permit some extra fittings to be included. In the rear part behind the cab there is a 200-h.p. steam winch, fitted with a steel hauling cable and capable of pulling virtually anything – even today the owner sometimes uses this winch to rescue modern heavy trucks from awkward situations where modern recovery vehicles cannot cope! At the rear a large 'spade' is fitted to the chassis which can be lowered into the ground to anchor the tractor when winching to the rear. The rope can also be paid out forwards and guide rollers may be seen by the front axle.

149 Sentinel 'S4' wagon No. 9075, built 1934, BEV 467

The Sentinel S series wagons which appeared in 1933 were magnificent vehicles which even today could, fully loaded, compete favourably with any modern truck of similar capacity. Numerous improvements were made to the earlier models to give a wagon capable of 60 m.p.h. and 120 b.h.p. with a econ-omical fuel consumption.

Externally the obvious difference is the flat-fronted, coach-built cab with doors incorporating sliding windows, full wind-screens with electric wipers and full electric lighting supplied by an engine-driven dynamo. Coal chutes are fitted in the cab roof (just visible above the nearside door). The boiler was basically the well-tried unit with only minor modifications and was fitted in the rear of the cab with a coal space fitted behind the crew seats on either side. The most interesting part of the S type is, however, hidden under the body. The engine, whilst in the usual place, is a four-cylinder poppet-valve unit mounted horizontally, in line with the chassis with the crankshaft linked via carden shaft-drive to a double reduction rear axle. A two-speed gear box is also built integrally with engine at the rear of the crankcase. Steam-assisted brakes are fitted to all wheels which were fitted originally with pnuematic tyres. Even an engine-driven tyre pump is fitted!

This was the final production design of the Sentinel and although even more advanced, powerful and fast experimental steam lorries were built home production ceased with the Second World War.

150 Tasker wagon No. 1915, built 1924, YB 183

The sole remaining example of a Tasker wagon. It is an overtype design with compound cylinders of $4\frac{1}{4}''$ and $6\frac{1}{2}''$ bore and $7''$ stroke and slide valves. The drive to the rear wheels is by chain and the rear axle has a band-type brake similar to the Foden design. The body is a tipper with a mechanically assisted hoist, driven by a chain from the flywheel. Note the brass tubes extending from the safety valves on the cylinder block to take any excess steam well above the cab and the grease guard in front of the driver to stop any oil thrown off the crankshaft and motion reaching the crew.

The very rare wagon is now owned by the Tasker Trust, having been restored to the condition seen here by the Tasker Company before their Museum was disbanded. At present (1970) it is receiving further attention to bring it back to full working order.

151 Thornycroft wagon No. 39, built 1899, AD 115, *Dorothy*

This wagon is one of the most interesting steam wagons still in existence. Apart from a steam van owned by Thornycrofts and an early Leyland wagon no other examples survive from this period in working order. The wagon is preserved in its original condition.

Features of note on this wagon are the totally unprotected driver's platform on which the vertical boiler (water-tube type) is mounted at the front with the chimney on top of it. The engine was built using the builders' experience as steam launch builders and is a horizontal compound engine mounted under the driver and fitted with a differential on the countershaft. The final drive to the rear wheels is by chain. The Ackermann steering is especially noteworthy as this was not generally adopted on steam vehicles for another thirty years but it will be noted the wagon's wheels are built in the traction engine style. A water tank is mounted at the rear of the chassis and the bodywork is a typical design for a brewer's dray of the period.

152 Yorkshire wagon No. 652, built 1914, U 2749

The Yorkshire steam wagon is most distinctive, with the boiler mounted right across the extreme front end of the chassis. The boiler itself is of an unusual design with the firebox in the centre section and a horizontal, tubed boiler barrel on either side. The hot gases and smoke from the fire pass through each barrel section through tubes in the lower half and then return to the central chimney via the upper set of tubes – there is no direct passage from the fire to the chimney. The firebox door is on the rear side of the boiler so it is fired by the driver or his fireman from the driving platform just behind the boiler unit. A pressure of 200 pounds per sq. inch is used. The engine is mounted behind the driver and across the chassis. It is a totally enclosed vertical compound of $5''$ and $7\frac{1}{2}''$ bores and $8''$ stroke. This drives through gears from the crankshaft and then by a chain to the rear wheels with much of the gearing exposed to the dust and mud under the chassis. Some later engines had a carden shaft drive and on these the engine was mounted in line with the chassis.

On this example steering is by a tram-like tiller on the nearside. The wheels are cast, but of hollow section to reduce weight, and are fitted with solid rubber tyres. The van body has been fitted in preservation days but is of authentic design of a carrier's wagon. Only three Yorkshire wagons are now known in Britain despite a production run from 1902 to 1937.

153 and 154 Garrett 'Suffolk Punch' tractor No. 33180, built 1918, BJ 4483

Only eight of the Garrett Suffolk Punch tractors were built and this is the sole survivor. It was intended for direct ploughing work, being designed at a time when large numbers of I.C.E.-engined tractors were coming into use on the land in competition with the steam engines.

This unusual machine has a chassis to support all the main units including the axles, the front one of which steers via Ackermann-type wheel steering. The boiler is, in effect, mounted backwards compared with normal practice as the firebox end is at the front by the driver, so that it is possible for him to tend the fire. Coal is carried behind the front panel. The compound-cylinder block is by the driver's left shoulder where the regulator lever may be seen (there is a double-high provision). The drive is taken via the balanced crankshaft which shows in red by the flywheel and gears to the back axle. At the rear the smokebox may be seen with below it the reserve water tank, mounting points for the towed ploughs and the guide rollers for the winching rope carried on the rear axle. The spoke design on the wheels is

also unusual and must help in keeping the weight down. No one should ever have any trouble identifying this engine at a rally!

155 Burrell crane engine No. 3829, built 1920, PB 9687, *His Majesty*

Unless an engine was going to be in constant use as a crane (see Plate 156) it was common practice to have an engine which could be used as a road locomotive if the jib was removed. This is a 8-n.h.p. Burrell road locomotive to which has been added a winch in front of the chimney and brackets just below the smokebox to fit the base of a crane jib. The drive to the winch is taken off the engine crankshaft by means of gears and the drive shaft which runs along the near side of the boiler barrel. Wider than average front wheels are fitted to help take the extra load which would cause ordinary wheels to sink in the ground.

156 Ransomes, Sims & Jefferies crane engine No. 31066, built 1921, PV 4393

Engines embodying cranes were frequently used to lift heavy machinery and one such use was in an engine builders works where items such as boilers and wheels had to be moved about. This engine is based on its maker's 6-n.h.p. traction engine and is believed to have been used for several years by its manufacturers in their works. The chimney, suitably reinforced, is utilised to form the jib section of the crane with a cable winch mounted just to its rear on top of the boiler. The winch is steam-driven via a drive from the crankshaft brought along the near side of the boiler and, to help with the very heavy steering that could result when lifting a big load, steam assistance is given to the steering as well. On this occasion the engine is lifting the rear wheel of a Burrell showmans engine.

157 **Robey 'Express' tractor No. 43165, built 1927, FE 9350, *Barbara***

Only a very few of these tractors were built and this is the sole survivor. It is based on the Robey steam wagon with an increased ground clearance and the large-diameter rear wheels usually associated with the winching tractors. The boiler is one of Robey's interesting pistol-type units with a circular, stayless firebox. The engine is a compound unit and almost totally enclosed as a protection against dust and dirt. There is a chain drive to the rear axle and additional water tanks are fitted to give the tractor a good working range. The cab roof is of the distinctive Robey shape which may be seen on other engines of the make. The high gearing of this tractor gives good road speeds and 25 m.p.h. is not at all uncommon.

158 **Mann steam cart No. 1287, built 1918, FU 5027, *Tiny Tim***

The Mann steam cart was an unusual design which could be used as a tractor or as a small wagon with a cart body fitted. The firm also constructed a longer chassis wagon but this was very much like the conventional overtype steam wagon.

The driving position is alongside the firebox on the off side with the firehole door in the side of the firebox so that the driver can tend the fire. This is the only crew space on the engine. Chain steering is fitted, controlled by the angled column in front of the driver, whilst the engine controls are arranged by the driver's left hand. The engine is a compound type coupled to an all-gear drive via four shafts to the rear axle which carries the differential. The flywheel is fitted on the nearside and governors allow belt work if required as the tractor could be used for agricultural work, including direct ploughing. The rear wheel spokes are of interest as they are cut from a single plate. On this example a large water tank and coal space is provided over the rear axle in the position the cart body could be fitted.

PART 4 THE PRESENT DAY

The Traction Engine Rally Movement

A firmly established country weekend activity in Britain during the summer months is the traction engine rally. These events now form the basis of the preservation movement, which started with enthusiasts interested in keeping steam traction engines for their own enjoyment holding gatherings. Today large crowds are attracted by the opportunity to see the engines in action again with great interest being shown in displays featuring engines doing the jobs they were built for, such as threshing corn, ploughing fields or rolling roads.

The first rally was held at the village of Appleford in Berkshire in 1951 following a race the previous year between two engine-owning enthusiasts on the same site. It was from this small start that the nationwide following has grown to a stage when, twenty years later, over eighty gatherings are now being held every summer. The annual Appleford rally is still a popular event attracting entries from a wide area although it has kept very strictly to its original concept of being a steam engine rally with few other attractions not connected with steam. Other events are run just as gatherings of enthusiasts whilst yet others have grown into huge shows showing every feature of past country life as well as introducing modern fairgrounds and entertainment that seems to have little connection with steam power.

To encourage the well-being of the movement the National Traction Engine Club in consultation with its affiliated societies has drawn up a voluntary Code of Practice for the guidance of organisers of steam engine rallies and its provisions are now accepted by all but a few organisers. The Code of Practice suggests standards for the conduct of events and methods of safeguarding the interests of owners and visitors alike. Its provisions have been drafted as a result of biannual conferences of rally organisers at which suggestions arising out of organisers' experiences in running events in one summer can often prove of use to everyone the following year. In this way organisers, engine-owners and the visitors are continually benefiting from others' experience and the general standards of rallies have improved greatly over the past decade.

One of the most important conditions on accepting the terms of the Code is that the organiser of a rally shall ensure that all the engines attending have been inspected in the past year by an insurance

F

inspector and have a current insurance against any failure of their boilers under pressure. Other points cover the safety of members of the public during events and races as well as the provision of adequate facilities on the display ground to cater for the large number of visitors. The number of traction engines in existence is not great in any limited area, so it is most important that rallies are not held either on the same day or within a week or two of each other in the same locality as this would make it very difficult for owners to attend both shows. It has to be remembered that owners take their engines out as a hobby and that it would be unreasonable to expect them to be away from home every weekend in the summer besides the fact it takes at least a day to prepare the engine for display and get it to the showground. Every winter much discussion is held over settling the following summer's programme with rally events of long standing receiving priority over recently started or new events when it comes to finally settling the dates. This service is of great help to the organiser as much abortive work and effort could result from events clashing. In many parts of the country, however, the number of events has now reached such a figure that the inclusion of any additional fixtures just is not possible without drastically affecting the long-standing rallies.

Rallies accepting the national Clubs Code of Practice are known as 'Approved Rallies' and are able to display as special device on their publicity. Lists of Approved Events are published each Spring and may be obtained from the National Traction Engine Club Secretary in exchange for the return postage and a small fee. A notable feature of the traction engine rally scene is that the events are run almost without exception for the engine-owner's enjoyment of his hobby with very little financial reward for his efforts other than a few sacks of coal. Many charities have however benefited from the engine-owners' efforts and it is this spirit which makes the rally field a really friendly place.

Societies for the Traction Engine Enthusiast

There are four national societies for the traction engine enthusiast and numerous smaller local clubs many of which hold regular meetings and organise rallies during the summer. The list below gives the addresses of the secretaries and is correct as at Autumn 1970 but as all are positions of a voluntary nature it is possible these may change from time to time.

National Organisations:

The National Traction Engine Club
   127 Greensted Road, Loughton, Essex.
   This club caters mainly for the rallying and active restoration of engines interests in the country.
The Road Locomotive Society
   136 Lavender Hill, Tonbridge, Kent.
   This society concentrates on the collection of information and data on engines and the membership is restricted to persons recommended by existing members.
Irish Steam Preservation Society
   W. F. Walsh-Kemmis, Ballykilcavan, Stradbally, Co. Laois, Eire.
Irish Steam Preservation Society (Ulster Branch)
   Mrs B. Boyd, Ballywindland, Ballymoney, Antrim, N. Ireland.
Scottish Traction Engine Society
   20 Geils Quadrant, Dumbarton, Dumbartonshire, Scotland.

Local Organisations:

Many local steam clubs are affiliated to the National Traction Engine Club whose list of affiliated clubs is reproduced here with their permission.

Banbury Steam Society
   19a Crouch Street, Banbury, Oxfordshire.
Bedford Steam Engine Preservation Society
   Field House, Turvey, Beds.
Chiltern Traction Engine Club
   Shepherds Hey, Green Lane, Radnage, High Wycombe, Bucks.
Cornish Traction Preservation Club
   20 Queens Park, Wadebridge, Cornwall.
County of Salop Steam Engine Society
   46 Sandford Avenue, Church Stretton, Salop.
Devon Traction Engine & Veteran Car Club
   17 Toronto Road, Exeter, Devon.
Dorset Steam & Historic Vehicle Club
   9 Waterlake, Stalbridge, Sturminster Newton, Dorset.

Fairford & District Steam Club
  9 The Plies, London Road, Fairford, Glos.
Hertfordshire Steam Preservation Society
  23 Nunnery Lane, Luton, Beds.
Hinckley Steam Appreciation Society
  1 Cedar Road, Earl Shilton, Leicester.
Lancashire Traction Engine Club
  2 Catterall Crescent, Bradshaw, Bolton, Lancs.
Lincolnshire Steam Engine Preservation Society
  Pansy Villa, Fulstow, Louth, Lincs.
Masham Traction Engine Club
  Deepdale, Market Place, Masham, Ripon, Yorks.
Morecambe Bay Traction Engine Club
  27 Norfolk Avenue, Morecambe, Lancs.
North of England Steam Traction Engine Society
  20 Church Street, Seaham, Co. Durham.
North Staffordshire & Cheshire Traction Engine Club
  Holcombe House, 173 Congleton Road, Biddulph, Stoke-on-Trent,
  Staffs.
'Old Steamers' Traction Engine Club
  17 Union Street, Oxford.
Seend Steam Preservation Club
  29 The Lye, Seend, Melksham, Wilts.
Somerset Traction Engine Club
  Perkham Field, Barton Road, Winscombe, Somerset.
South Yorkshire Traction Engine Club
  17a Spa Lane, Woodhouse, Sheffield, Yorks.
Thames Valley Traction Engine Club
  19 Bridle Path, Woodcote, Reading, Berks.
Three Counties Steam Preservation Society
  Oak View, Beech Hill, Headley, Bordon, Hants.
Warwickshire Steam Engine Society
  7 Highland Road, Lillington, Leamington Spa, Warwicks.
Welland Valley Vintage Traction Club
  4 Adam & Eve Street, Market Harborough, Leics.
West of England Steam Engine Society
  87 Roskear Road, Cambourne, Cornwall.
Worthing & Southern Counties Historic Vehicle Group
  24 Sheridan Road, Worthing, Sussex.

The following clubs are not affiliated to the National Traction Engine Club:

Bysteam
   Brookview, Bawburgh, Norfolk.
Great Yorkshire Traction Engine Club
   East Villa, Eastfield Road, Pickering, Yorks.
Leeds & District Traction Engine Club
   93 Woodside Road, Wyke, Bradford, Yorks.
Norfolk Steam Engine Club
   4 Wilderness Lane, Harleston, Norfolk.
The Steam Plough Club
   3 Ridge Side, Haw Lane, Bledlow Ridge, High Wycombe, Bucks.
The East Anglian Traction Engine Club
   2 South View, Radwinter, Saffron Walden, Essex.

Colour Slides

As a service to clubs and lecturers on this subject, the colour plates in this volume are also available as colour slides from *The Slide Centre, 17 Brodrick Road, London, S.W.17*. The slides are 35 mm in $2'' \times 2''$ mounts and are suitable for all standard slide projectors and viewers, price $12\frac{1}{2}$p each. Quote the title of the book and the plate numbers when ordering.

Museums Exhibiting Traction Engines

It is most unfortunate that there is no national museum with a fully representative selection of steam traction engines and wagons. Some provincial museums, however, have exhibits as well as some private collections which are open to the public on restricted opening hours, details of which would be available from the owners.

Bicton Countryside Museum, Budleigh Salterton, Devon.
   Traction engine, portable and a road roller on view as well as some agricultural items.
Bressingham Hall, Diss, Norfolk
   Fourteen different types of engine are on show ranging from ploughing engines and a showmans engine to portables. Engines are in steam on restricted opening days. Many railway engines are also on show and a steam roundabout.
Belfast Transport Museum
   Rollers, traction engine and road locomotive on exhibition.
Birmingham Museum of Transport and Industry

Road roller and other steam plant are put in steam on special opening days although visible on any weekday.

Cheddar Motor Museum, Cheddar, Somerset
Tractor and portable engines on view.

G. Cushing Collection, Thursford, Norfolk
A private collection of numerous steam engines and organs open most summer Sundays.

Irish Steam Preservation Society Museum, Stradbally, Co. Laois
Includes many steam engines and models.

Montagu Motor Museum, Beaulieu, Hampshire
Showmans engine on view; also an annual rally.

Museum of Transport, Glasgow
Has remains of an early steam carriage and models.

Science Museum, Kensington, London
Early Aveling & Porter engine and several good models.

In addition to this list there are several small museums which have collections of photographs and other details of steam traction engines. There are also several schemes at present unfulfilled to exhibit collections of engines, a notable one being the Tasker Trust which is raising funds to provide an exhibition building for a big collection of Tasker engines at present held in store near Winchester. Enquiries about the Trust should be directed to Russell House, East Street, Andover, Hampshire.

Further Reading

Through this book I have only been able to give a very brief outline of the history of traction engines and steam wagons with the descriptions of the engines written in a manner that the ordinary interested rally visitor will, I hope, understand. In the course of the years many very interesting books have been written on the subject, whilst maker's catalogues are a fascinating source of information if they can be found. During the preparation of this volume many reference sources have been tapped, and so I append a list of books the reader might wish to study as I have found them useful.

Apprenticeship in Steam – J. Hampshire (J. H. Lake 1969).
The Bressingham Book – A. Bloom (Jarrold 1970).
A Century of Traction Engines – W. J. Hughes (David & Charles 1970).

Chronicles of a Country Works (Burrells of Thetford) – R. H. Clark (Percival Marshall 1952).

Commercial Road Vehicles – E. L. Cornwell (Batsford 1960).

Commercial Vehicles – E. L. Cornwell (Ian Allan 1963).

The Development of the English Traction Engine – R. H. Clark (Goose & Son 1959).

The Development of the English Steam Wagon – R. H. Clark (Goose & Son 1963).

Discovering Traction Engines – H. Bonnett (Shire Publications 1969).

Fowler Steam Road Vehicles – W. J. Hughes (David & Charles 1970).

Garretts of Leiston – R. A. Whitehead (Percival Marshall 1964).

A Hundred Years of Road Rollers (Aveling Barford Ltd.) – (Oakwood Press 1965).

I Worked with Traction Engines – J. Hampshire (J. H. Lake 1968).

The Lure of the Traction Engine – (North Staffs & Cheshire T. E. Club).

Military Transport of World War I – C. Ellis & D. Bishop (Blandford 1970).

Modern Manual for Steam Road Vehicle Drivers – W. M. Salmon (M.A.P. 1967).

Old Motor Magazine – Old Motor Ltd, Various issues 1962–1968.

Saga of the Steam Plough – H. Bonnett (Allen & Unwin 1965).

Showmans Engines – W. Pickles (Oakwood Press).

A Simple History of the Steam Engine – J. D. Storer (John Baker 1969).

Steam Engine Builders of Lincolnshire – R. H. Clark (Goose & Son 1955).

'Steaming' – Quarterly journal of the National Traction Engine Club.

The Steam Lorry – R. W. Kinder (Oakwood Press 1956).

The Taskers Collection Sale Catalogue – (Christie, Manson & Woods 1969).

The Traction Engine – F. H. Gillford, (Oakwood Press 1966).

The Traction Engine Register – (Worthing & Southern Counties Historic Vehicle Group 1968).

Traction Engines – P. Wright (Adam & Charles Black 1959).

Traction Engines in the North – David Joy (Dalesman Pub. Co. 1970).

Traction Engines Worth Modelling – W. J. Hughes (David & Charles 1969).

Veteran & Vintage Magazine – Various issues.

Waterloo Ironworks (Taskers History) – L. T. C. Rolt (David & Charles 1969).
Numerous Rally Programmes which are a constant source of information.

GLOSSARY

Every traction engine is built up from numerous small parts, many of which have special names or are fitted for specific reasons. Several of these parts are shown on the diagram of a general-purpose type engine but many are missing, since they are either not visible on that particular elevation or are not fitted to that type of engine. In order that the non-technical reader may know the meaning of the part names and the purpose they serve this glossary of terms has been included for reference when reading the descriptions of the engines illustrated in the colour section.

Ackermann steering. Ackermann steering is the type of steering used on most cars and lorries. The wheels turn on the ends of the axle beam whilst the axle itself remains stationary. This more positive type of steering was fitted to most later types of steam wagon such as the Sentinels and will also be seen on the Thornycroft of 1899 (plate 151).

Ashpan. By law traction engines should not have any fire visible from the firebox and ashes must not be dropped on the road. The ashpan collects the ashes as they fall from the grate and is the lowest part of the firebox unit.

Bearing brasses. The journals in which any shaft on a traction engine runs are fitted with adjustable brass inserts to take up any wear. They may be clearly seen at the crankshaft end on the engine in plate 33.

Belly tanks. To give extra water-carrying capacity, especially on road engines, additional tanks were slung on either side of the boiler barrel. These 'belly tanks' were connected to the tender tank.

Boilers. There are several different types of boilers on traction engines and steam wagons with the locomotive type the most common. This type is described in detail in the chapter on how the engine works.

Vertical type boilers. These are used on undertype steam wagons in the main. They consist of an outer water jacket enclosing a round in section firebox which is fired normally from the top. Water tubes cross the upper fire space and connect with the water jacket and superheaters are sometimes fitted.

Fire-tubes. These are used in locomotive-type boilers and are the tubes carrying the hot gases from the fire to the chimney which are surrounded by water.

Water-tubes. As used in vertical-type boilers. The water passes through tubes placed in the flow of gases from the fire to the chimney.

Boiler pressure. The pressure on every square inch of the surface of the inside of the boiler exerted by the steam trapped therein. It is normally expressed in pounds per sq. inch.

Cab or Canopy. The name given to the roof covering all or part of the engine.

Chain Steering. The method most commonly used on traction engines and older wagons. A chain, connected to each axle end, is wound around a roller mounted on the bottom front side of the firebox. Rotation of the roller by means of the steering wheel winds the chain on and off, pulling in on one side and letting off on the other, thus pulling the steering round. There are often forty turns from one steering lock to the other!

Compensating gear. An alternative name for the differential.

Compound cylinders. Many traction engines and wagons have a two-cylinder arrangement or 'compound' method of working. The cylinders are of different diameters, the smaller one taking steam at boiler pressure to work the piston. When this first cylinder exhausts the steam it is probably around half its original pressure and is passed into the second, larger cylinder to work the piston in that cylinder before being exhausted to the chimney. In effect the steam is used twice, giving greater efficiency and more economic working.

Crosshead and crosshead guides. The crosshead is the link between the piston rod and the connecting rod. To keep the piston rod running precisely the crosshead runs in guideways called the crosshead guides.

Cylinder drain cocks. Taps with a connection to each end of the cylinder so that any water condensing in the cylinder may be drained away.

Crankshaft. The shaft carrying the flywheel which converts the reciprocating motion of the piston into the rotational movement needed to turn the wheels.

Damper. The adjustable flap at the front of the ashpan which regulates the amount of air reaching the fire.

Double-crank compound engine. A compound working engine with separate connecting rods from each cylinder. The crankshaft has two cranks on it set at 90 degrees to each other giving four power strokes per revolution.

Double-high. Many compound working engines have an arrangement whereby boiler pressure steam may be used in both cylinders at once. This gives extra power which can be used when starting with a big load.

Drawbar, Drawpins. The bar and pins used to couple trailers to the engine. The bar is fitted at the rear of the tender. Several engines also have a fitting by the smokebox used to push trailers into position.

Driving pins. These pins connect the axle to the rear wheels and may be seen in the bulge-like extension to the rear hub. Removal of the pins disconnects the drive and enables the axle to be used as a winch, as many engines carry a wire rope on the rear axle.

Duplex engine. A twin-cylinder engine but with cylinders of equal diameter both using boiler pressure steam.

Fairleads. This is a name for the guide rollers for a winching rope which may be seen on the tender of many engines.

Feed pumps. Small water pumps which are normally driven off the crankshaft to force-feed the water into the boiler from the tender or belly tanks. Plate 103 shows an example on a road roller.

Firebox, Fire-tubes. For a description see the details of boilers.

Flywheel. Flywheels are fitted on the crankshaft and are normally very heavy to fulfill their purpose of keeping the engine turning over smoothly. Often they have a wide outer edge so that a driving belt can be fitted.

Fore carriage. This is the name given to the whole front assembly of the engine, axle and wheels, which is steerable.

Governors. The governor regulates the supply of steam from the boiler automatically to keep the engine running at a pre-set constant speed when driving machines or a dynamo by means of a belt from the flywheel. It is usually set high up on the cylinder block and driven by means of a small, leather belt from the crank-shaft.

Hornplates. The extension of the firebox side plates to support the motion work.

Horsepower. Nominal horsepower (n.h.p.) is quoted for most traction engines but this bears no relation to the actual horsepower produced by the engine in good working order. The term is believed to have originated in the days of portable engines when farmers required some idea of the work the engine could do. In later years the term merely indicates the relative size of the engine.

Injector. The injector is normally positioned on one side of the tender near to the bottom and adjacent to the water tank. It is a device which, by means of boiler steam, is able to force-feed the water from the tank into the boiler. Its action is not easy to explain without diagrams and is best demonstrated on an engine.

Lubricator. A mechanical lubricator will be found on nearly all engines mounted near to the top of the cylinder block. It is driven from the piston rod or valve rod and supplies measured quantities of special oil to the cylinder and valve gear. Most steam vehicles have a total loss system of lubrication from their motion work which calls for frequent visits by the oil can to all moving parts.

Lagging. The boilers of traction engines are lagged around the barrel section with wood slats covered with thin sheet-metal plates which can be painted. The object is to reduce heat losses especially in winter.

Manholes. Inspection manholes are often fitted in the boiler barrel so that full internal inspections can be made from time to time. A good example may be seen in plate 9.

Mudholes. In their working days engines often had to lift water into their boilers from muddy streams or ponds with a result that quantities of fine mud would find their way into the firebox. If these deposits built up they could fill the water space and cause the plates to become red hot and possibly fail under pressure. The mud holes are fitted around the base of the firebox (see diagram) so that the mud could be washed out from time to time.

The motion work. An expression used to describe all the moving parts between the cylinder block and the crankshaft.

Overtype. Steam wagons with locomotive-type boilers and the motion in the usual traction engine style were known as overtype wagons.

Perch bracket. The perch bracket is the link between the smokebox and the front axle on an engine.

Piston. The part within the cylinder which is moved back and forth by the steam pressure. It is an exact sliding fit.

Piston valves. A valve system which uses a piston acting in a cylinder alongside the main cylinder of the engine to operate the valves which admit the steam to the cylinder. An example may be seen in plate 108.

Plug. On all engines there is fitted into the top of the firebox a brass plug of which the centre is filled with lead. This is a safety device to protect the boiler from overheating should the water level in the boiler fall below a level which covers the firebox completely. Should the water level drop, the firebox top, or crown, will soon become red hot and weaken but in this case the lead will melt out of the brass plug, allow the steam to come into the firebox and put out the fire. Dropping a plug is a driver's greatest embarrassment!

Poppet valves. Some high-speed wagon engines use poppet valves to admit and exhaust the steam from the cylinders. The action is similar to the valves in a motor car engine.

Priming. This is a term used to describe the emission of water as well as steam from the funnel. It is usually due to the boiler being overfilled, with a result that the boiler water floods up into the top of the boiler and passes through the regulator into the cylinders. As water is incompressible it can cause great damage in the cylinder and valve chest. A similar action sometimes occurs on an engine travelling down a steep hill which a resulting loss of braking power.

Regulator. This is the gear which controls the admission of the boiler steam into the cylinder block and thus the speed of the engine. It is operated from the driver's stand by means of a lever.

Reversing lever. A description of the working of the reversing lever and gear will be found in the section on how an engine works.

Safety valves. The safety valves are fitted at the highest point in the boiler system which is under pressure, usually on the top of the cylinder block. They are pre-set to the maximum safe normal working pressure of the engine and work automatically should the pressure rise too high.

Scarifier. Many rollers are fitted with scarifiers and an example may be seen in plate 104. They are used to cut up an old road surface, being operated by means of a large hand wheel on their sides which lowers the tines (large, chisel-like pieces of iron which are fitted in the base) into the road surface).

Scenic showmans engines. For a description see the section on showmans road locomotives.

Single-crank compound engine. This type of engine was patented by Burrells in 1889 and was a most successful design. The engine works as a compound but has only a single crank on the crankshaft giving two power strokes per revolution. An example is shown in plate 13.

Slide valve. This is the most common type of valve used on traction engines. It is a plate with steam channels cut into it which is made a sliding fit against the outer side of the main cylinder. The plate slides back and forth across ports in the cylinder wall, the movement being controlled by the valve gear. When the channels cut in the slide coincide with the ports steam is admitted to the cylinder or exhausted to the chimney as required.

Speed pinions. Very few engines have a single speed, most having two and road locomotives usually three. The change speed pinions are mounted on the crankshaft and second shaft and are taken in and out of mesh by means of levers. Changes may only be made when the engine is at a standstill. The levers may be seen in plate 67.

Springing. Many rollers, ploughing engines and some traction engines are unsprung. Engines designed for road use are often sprung by means of leaf springs on the rear axle. Wagons are usually better sprung with the more modern examples being fitted with normal lorry springs.

Spuds, Spud pan. In wet weather engines have great difficulty in gripping on mud and so bolt on 'spuds' can be fitted to the rear wheels as shown in plate 53. These spuds cannot be used on the highway.

The spud pan to hold the spuds is a fitting on the front axle and may be seen in plate 24.

Stays. The firebox of an engine consists, in simple terms, of an inner and an outer steel box with the water space in between. To serve the dual purpose of locating the inner firebox and to give some support to the large areas of the side plates stays are fitted at frequent intervals between the two boxes. These are screwed into place and the outer ends may be seen on many of the colour plates giving a cushion-like effect to the firebox side plates.

Strakes. The plates fixed to the rear wheels of traction engines to help give some grip are known as strakes.

Superheaters. Ordinary traction engines use steam collected just above the boiler water level which contains a good number of water droplets and is known as 'wet' steam. Some steam wagons with high-speed engines find this sort of steam unsuitable due to condensation troubles and so a superheater is fitted in the upper firebox space to dry the steam. It consists of a coil of tubes through which the steam is passed to boil off any water droplets held in it.

Tender tank. A supply of water for the boiler is carried in the tender water tank fitted below the driver's stand and coal space.

Top dead centre. When an engine stops with the piston at its furthest points of travel in the cylinder, the operating rods and the crank on the crankshaft will all be in line. In this position it is impossible for the engine to be restarted, as any pressure of steam on the piston will not be able to throw over the crank unless the crankshaft is moved round a few degrees by pushing the flywheel round. The situation, known as stopping on dead centre, is only possible with single-cylinder or single-crank compound engines.

Tubes. See the reference under boilers.

Tyres. Most general-purpose engines retain the steel tyres and strakes fitted to the engines when new. Rubber tyres were invented in the middle of the last century and used with limited success, mainly due to the poor quality of the rubber. Improvements over the years brought about the general use of rubber solid tyres on road engines soon after the First World War and pneumatic tyres on wagons were common after 1930. Solid-rubber strip tyres are either bolted to the wheel or are made in a continuous strip which is pressed onto the wheel rim from the side.

Undertypes. Steam wagons with their engines mounted below the chassis frame level are known as undertypes.

Valve gear. Descriptions of the various forms of valve gear will be found under piston valves, slide valves and in the section on how the traction engine works.

Water level gauges. It is important that the driver knows the water level in his boiler and gauges are fitted and usually duplicated on the firebox to indicate this. A simple design may be seen in plate 4.

Water lifter. The water lifter is used to lift water from a static tank, pond or similar source into the engine's tanks. It is worked by passing boiler steam across the end of a suction hose, thus creating a suction in the hose which lifts the water up the pipe. The coiled suction hose will be noted on several of the engines.

Water pocket. In the event of the engine having to be filled by a hose or bucket water pockets are provided on the water tanks. An example can be seen on the belly tank in plate 81.

Winding drum. The winding, or winching, drum will be noted inside of the rear nearside wheel on many traction engines and road locomotives. It is fastened to the rear axle. and may be operated when the driving pin disconnects the drive to the rear wheel. It forms a very powerful winch.

INDEX

Figures in bold type are those of the colour plate numbers. Page numbers are given for references to text.